MW00800423

AWAKENING

THE DIVINE FEMININE WITHIN

A SELF-GUIDED JOURNAL FOR HEALING YOUR INNER
CHILD, RECLAIMING YOUR SOVEREIGNTY,
AND MANIFESTING YOUR DREAMS

CLAUDIA BYKOWSKI & SASHA CARMICHAEL

WE WOULD LIKE TO ACKNOWLEDGE the incredible wisdom that lives through the words of Alan Watts and Abraham Hicks, as well as Dr. Joe Dispenza and Dr. Robert Gilbert for providing the long forgotten science bridging the physical world to the spiritual realms, Paul Stamets and Michael Pollen for pioneering the way of Plant Medicine use in the modern world, and finally Matías De Stefano and Kaia Ra for the courage in telling their stories that have inspired so many. Thank you.

A SPECIAL SHOUTOUT OF GRATITUDE to Samantha Bruce for her exquisite artistry in visual storytelling. Your magic has brought this journal to life in a way that exceeded all expectations.

"MAYBE THE JOURNEY ISN'T SO MUCH ABOUT BECOMING ANYTHING. MAYBE IT'S ABOUT UNBECOMING EVERYTHING THAT ISN'T REALLY YOU, SO YOU CAN BE WHO YOU WERE MEANT TO BE IN THE FIRST PLACE." — *Paul Coelho*

NOTE FROM THE AUTHORS

As two women who are on their path of awakening their inner power and sovereignty, our mission is to spread light on the shadow of the collective consciousness and pave a new path to a paradigm of freedom, empowerment, and authentic expression. As the evolution of human consciousness continues, we are collectively waking up to the fact that feminine repression has been at play for centuries and is still going on today.

In ancient times, Feminine Power was honored, celebrated, and played a large role in societal structures of flourishing civilizations. But as we transitioned into the modern era, Patriarchy emerged. The Masculine dominated the world with power, control, and violence, while the intuitive, divine, energetic, and spiritual side of life was suppressed. Organized religion arose and was masqueraded as the path to truth; those that practiced mysticism, alchemy, astrology, or divination were driven underground and were labeled as "Black Magicians", witches, and heretics. Many people were burned alive as a result of adopting beliefs outside of the church. This trend continued to evolve in the psyche and has resulted in many feminine victims of violence, sexual and physical abuse, silencing, suppression, manipulation, and intimidation.

We are overjoyed to be embarking on this healing and empowerment journey with you, as we explore new depths of peace within. By remembering who you are, you become a part of the healing of the collective consciousness. Together, we pave the path into a better world where freedom, prosperity, unconditional love, and truth can thrive.

— *Claudia & Sasha*

DISCLAIMER:

THE CONTENT OF THIS BOOK IS FOR INFORMATION AND EDUCATIONAL PURPOSES ONLY. The content within this journal is designed to encourage self-reflection and self-realization. The journal prompts and exercises provided are intended to be thought-provoking and supportive, but they should not replace professional advice or therapy. If you are experiencing severe emotional distress, mental health issues, or any physical discomfort, it is crucial to seek appropriate medical or professional help.

To find additional resources and support on this journey please visit us at our website and social channels.

www.eloah369.com
Instagram - @divinefemininejournal
YouTube - @awakeningthedivinefeminine

OVERVIEW | OUR PHILOSOPHY

We believe in the Universal Law: As Above So Below, As Within So Without. If our inner child is hurting and energy is stuck in our body's memory from traumatic experiences, not only will our outer reality reflect what's going on internally, but we will have less energy to bring our creative desires and manifestations to life.

This guidebook serves as a path to reprogramming your subconscious through four sections:

CONNECTING TO THE PRESENT MOMENT | MEETING YOUR INNER CHILD
DANCING WITH YOUR SHADOW | MANIFESTING YOUR DREAMS

Each section is intentionally designed to work with your energy centers (the chakras), starting from the first chakra (the root) and ending at the seventh chakra (the crown). As we work up the chakra system, more and more of your vital life force energy will be freed from blockages and restored to its natural flow. This is when manifestation starts to happen rapidly as you bring yourself into alignment with the Universe's natural rhythm. These internal changes will affect your outer reality, and with a little diligence and commitment, your life starts to transform before your eyes.

While many have woken up to the fact that we are spiritual beings having a human experience, our human vessel is made up of a magical, cosmic coalescence of the Mind, Body & Spirit. We hope to balance all 3 aspects through energetic alignment with our HIGHER SELF, which is the wise being within you. Your higher self is the version of you that is unencumbered by the ego in the non-material dimension of you (some call it a soul or spirit) that's part of the cosmic or celestial whole. Think of it as your soul's essence. Our HIGHER SELF can serve as a valuable source of guidance and wisdom for us as we navigate challenges on our journeys through the 3D realm.

Self-love and self-acceptance are the pillars of our healing, empowerment, and manifestation method. Once a person has reclaimed and recognized the worth within themselves, how could they not be sovereign and abundant? You will become empowered and confident within yourself and your capabilities because you've put in the work to create them. Once you are standing in this powerful place within yourself, you have the ability to create your dream reality because you become a conduit of energy that attracts that which you are.

By creating a simple daily practice that fosters profound self-love, you will cultivate a stronger and more fulfilling connection with yourself, and you will naturally begin to vibrate at a higher frequency. Effortlessly, you will begin to attract higher vibe people, places, and things into your life.

Our intention with this journal is to demystify the Law of Attraction so your highest potential can manifest into your reality. Through this process, you will develop a greater sense of self-reliance, as you invest time in understanding your true essence and soul's wishes. The love you hold for yourself will inspire you to consistently make wiser decisions that benefit your own path and well-being. Eventually, this inner transformation will reflect in the external world, attracting the dream life you've always envisioned, as the state within yourself mirrors the reality around you. However, it is crucial to embody the habits and qualities of your Higher Self before expecting your dream reality to materialize.

As you embark on the journey to expand your consciousness, the Universe will present you with challenges to test your progress, yet it will never overwhelm you beyond your capabilities. When faced with difficult or frightening situations, it's helpful to perceive them as opportunities for growth. By navigating through these tests, you will begin to discover the deeper wisdom they hold and learn from them more swiftly, gradually reducing their triggering impact. You are steadily progressing towards a harmonious state of existence known as "flow state". Your consciousness is expanding; your vibration is rising.

We are always forgetting and remembering who we are once again. This journal isn't an all-encompassing solution for negative thoughts and emotions, but rather a tool and a reminder of who you are and how to get back to your most authentic essence. We highly encourage slowly incorporating these practices as a part of your daily life and staying as consistent as makes sense for you.

As you embark on this journey toward unconditional love and sovereignty, coming to full acceptance of where you are on your path in this exact moment is the key to beginning your transformation with a solid foundation. You can't shame or guilt yourself into a life of more love, abundance, joy, and fulfillment. When we operate from a place of fear and unacceptance, the changes that we make will be temporary and unsustainable.

The first section in this journal includes practices and tools that will help you become grounded in acceptance for where you are right now.

"WHEREVER
YOU ARE IS THE
ENTRY POINT."

— *Kabir*

JOURNAL
AWARENESS: WHERE ARE YOU NOW?

WHAT FEELINGS AND EMOTIONS ARE YOU EXPERIENCING IN YOUR
REALITY RIGHT NOW?

_____

_____

_____

_____

_____

_____

HOW CAN YOU GIVE YOURSELF GRACE AND ACCEPTANCE IN THIS
MOMENT?

_____

_____

_____

_____

_____

DESCRIBE IN DETAIL THE VERSION OF YOURSELF YOU'D LIKE TO
BECOME.

_____

_____

_____

_____

_____

_____

_____

_____

WHAT IS YOUR INTENTION FOR THE JOURNEY YOU ARE ABOUT TO EMBARK ON?

Solfeggio Scale Frequency with Corresponding Chakras

It is said that when all the chakras are balanced, we can step into our highest potential and operate at our highest level. We can feel happy, healthy, and whole:

The Solfeggio Frequency Scale refers to specific tones of sound that help stimulate your mind and body health. These frequencies are said to have been used by the ancients in both Western and Eastern cultures as a way of healing.

A researcher named Dr. Joseph Puleo is credited with rediscovering these frequencies in the 1970s and bringing them back into the public eye. Due to perfect mathematical aspects we couldn't even pretend to understand, the Solfeggio Frequencies are believed to have profound effects on the conscious and subconscious mind, stimulating healing and vitality throughout the entire body. We strongly recommend using these frequencies on your journey through this journal as they not only can help you clear and balance your chakras but also help your mind enter a meditative state much faster. While there are many ways to balance the chakras, Solfeggio Sound Therapy is easily executed. All you need are headphones, a private space to meditate, and the Youtube App. Scan the QR codes to the guided meditations we've created for each section or search the internet for the specific frequencies listed below as you are working with the corresponding chakra.

396 Hz - This tone is associated with the **Root Chakra**. The root chakra is associated with our safety, security, and survival. The 396 hz tone removes negative blocks and fears from the subconscious and dissipates feelings of guilt and shame. It boosts your power to achieve and unlocks inner peace. This tone also contains within it the magical numbers 3,6, and 9, said by Tesla himself to be the keys to the Universe.

417 hz - This tone is associated with the Sacral Chakra. It is known as the facilitator of change. It can release trauma that has been stored in the body and is powerful enough to undo negative outcomes caused by negative thought and behavior patterns.

528 hz - This tone is associated with the Solar Plexus Chakra and is used to tune up your self-confidence and self-esteem. This is the sound of positive transformation and miracles.

639 hz - This tone is the frequency of the heart, also known as the Heart Chakra. This universal key frequency enables intimacy and vulnerability. It is helpful in healing relationships, communication, understanding, tolerance, and LOVE.

741 hz - This frequency promotes expression and solutions, helping to unblock and balance the Throat Chakra, the chakra of creation. There is a saying "closed mouths don't get fed" - let's start speaking up, lovely!

852 hz - Associated with the **Third Eye Chakra** tone. 852 hz will help you connect to your intuition, perhaps your feminine's strongest superpower. It raises awareness, helps cut through illusions, and channels powerful guidance on your path.

963 hz - The **Crown Chakra** is your connection to Source, the Divine, God, and the Universe. Again, you see the powerful numbers 3,6, and 9 in this frequency. This sound allows your spirit to return to oneness, reminding us we have never actually been separate at all.

SECTION ONE:
Connecting To The Present Moment

What is Meditation & Why Do We Do It?

Meditation is a practice of calming the mind, simply put. Not only can it give you a sense of peace and balance that can have positive effects on your physical and emotional well-being, it is also the doorway into the subconscious mind.

The subconscious mind controls 95% of our reality. If you were a computer, the subconscious would be all the automatic programming running in the hard drive that you aren't able to see. The more awareness you can bring to your subconscious mind, the more you will be able to "override" the programs you are automatically functioning on. Going into the subconscious to make "edits" and reprogramming your mind will slowly change your reality. Bringing awareness to how you think means consciously choosing the thoughts and emotions you want to experience and removing negative thought patterns.

Meditation allows you to shift your focus from the rational mind to your heart and intuition, allowing for coherence that creates a deeper connection to your true direction and purpose in life. It's a powerful tool that helps you align with your authentic self and lead a more fulfilling and meaningful existence.

Meditation for beginners can be uncomfortable and frustrating at first, but just like anything, practice makes perfect. And if you are a pro, then you already know how rewarding it can be; feel free to skip to the next section if you feel like you've got the basics down.

"MEDITATION IS NOT ABOUT STOPPING THOUGHTS, BUT RECOGNIZING THAT WE ARE MORE THAN OUR THOUGHTS & FEELINGS."

— *Arianna Huffington*

"QUIET THE MIND AND THE SOUL WILL SPEAK."

— *Ma Jaya Sati Bhagavati*

- Sit in a comfortable position in a private area or room, or outside in nature if you wish.
- Scan the QR Code above to the guided meditation or use a Binaural Beat Meditation soundtrack by searching for one you like via Spotify or Youtube.
- Focus on your breath. Slowly begin to inhale as deeply as feels comfortable. Try breathing all the way down into the pit of your belly, filling up your chest last.
- Calm your mind and become aware of your thoughts. As thoughts swirl around, try to simply notice them but don't take them anywhere.
- Breathe in and breathe out.
- Notice and dismiss.

- Imagine your brain as an empty sky, a sunrise, sunset, or clear blue, and your thoughts as paper airplanes that you are watching fly in and out of your headspace (sky).
- Breathe in slowly for 4 counts, exhale slowly for 4 counts.
- Notice and dismiss.
- Imagine your sky becoming more clear. Gradually dismissing more and more paper airplanes, creating more space. You are slowly "emptying your mind."
- Repeat this practice until the end of this video.
- End your session with kindness. Thank yourself for your time and effort.

Congrats! You have officially consciously recognized what's going on in your own head! The intention here is to make it easier and more comfortable for you to take a look at what's going on within your mind, as our thoughts are the fundamental building blocks for our realities. As you progress through this journal, you will get better at calming your conscious mind and bringing more awareness to your subconscious. This is the practice that the rest of the practices will piggyback off of, so try to get this down first. Take as much time as you need, and be kind to yourself along the way.

ROOT CHAKRA
SAFETY, GROUNDING, AND THE RIGHT TO LIVE

ELEMENT: **EARTH**
COLOR: **RED**

We will now practice Grounding, connecting to the Earth, and our Root Chakra.

The Root Chakra is the first and lays the foundation for the rest of the chakras to expand. It is connected to our basic survival needs such as food, shelter, and financial stability.

If the Root Chakra is out of balance or blocked, we have a "shaky" foundation; we may feel unsafe, unstable, or unsure in our existence. We may even feel threatened, as if we're standing on unstable ground.

When the Root Chakra is open and activated, we feel confident in our ability to withstand challenges and stand on our own two feet. It is important to unblock and balance this chakra first on our journey up the chakra system.

GUIDED MEDITATION #2
CREATE YOUR SAFETY NEST

Begin by creating your safe place; you can create a cocoon, a nest, a sanctuary, or whatever it is that represents the ultimate safe place in your mind. Get creative! Is it a nest made from branches nestled in an enchanted forest with magical creatures and plant life surrounding you? Or is it a lofty Rapunzel Palace hidden away in the clouds decorated with your favorite furs, pillows, and furry companions?

- Let's begin by getting into a comfortable position in a private area or room, or outside in nature if you wish.
- Scan the QR code to the guided meditation above or use a Binaural 396 hz Frequency via Spotify or Youtube.
- Focus on your breath and begin inhaling and exhaling.
- Try to channel your breath as deep into your belly as feels comfortable.
- In your mind, begin to visualize your safety nest. What sounds do you hear? What scents do you smell? How does it feel?
- Find the feeling of safety within.
- Visualize yourself sitting in this magical place. Now shift your awareness to your root chakra, the area between your perineum and lower spine.
- Imagine a glowing red ball of energy below your spine, connecting you to the ground you are sitting on.
- Welcome it, observe it. What does it feel like? Can you feel the sensation of your grounded connection to the earth?

- Do you feel supported? Do you feel safe?
- If there are any emotions that come up, let them rise and drain any pain that needs to be released.
- Send a healing stream of your energy down to your root chakra. This can look like a team of fairies or a glowing gold stream of energy, whatever comes naturally.
- Send a message down to it - tell your root chakra that it is safe. Tell it that you are connected to the Earth and that you are held and protected by her.
- FEEL that connection.
- Feel your body firmly planted to the ground. Feel the stability of Mother Earth that is holding you up.
- Now imagine that the energy in the chakra begins to expand, and the red light emanating from it fills your entire safe place. Feel the warmth and protection all around you. Let this sensation show you that you are abundant, supported, and held by Mother Earth.

Repeat this practice often, especially during times of stress, anxiety, worry, or desperation. During times of stress, it is most important to ground and remember your connection to the earth. Your nest is always ready and waiting for you.

ROOT CHAKRA AWARENESS

WHEN THE WORLD FEELS CHAOTIC, HOW CAN I REMAIN ROOTED FIRMLY TO THE GROUND?

_____

_____

_____

_____

_____

IN WHAT WAYS DOES MY BODY ALWAYS TAKE CARE OF ME?

_____

_____

_____

_____

WHAT DOES IT MEAN TO ME TO BE FIRMLY ROOTED IN THE PRESENT MOMENT?

_____

_____

_____

_____

_____

_____

_____

_____

_____

BREATHE IT IN. LOVE. YOU ARE HOME.

As we move through this journey, we will begin the practice of writing positive affirmations. These affirmations will help you to reprogram your subconscious and shift your mindset from lack, self-doubt, and instability to abundance, prosperity, and empowerment!

When you regularly practice these affirmations, you will inevitably build a stronger belief in yourself. This will lead to improved performance, resilience, and courage to fearlessly go after the life of your dreams. **Let's begin.**

ROOT CHAKRA AFFIRMATIONS

I AM HOME ON EARTH WITH MY
BELOVED FAMILY ALL AROUND ME.

I AM NOURISHED FROM ALL DIRECTIONS,
AND I WILL BE CARED FOR UNTIL THE DAY
I LEAVE THIS EARTH.

I AM WORTHY OF ABUNDANCE
AND FINANCIAL SECURITY.

I AM EQUIPPED WITH ALL THE
TOOLS I NEED TO SUCCEED.

I AM AT HOME IN MY BODY, AND I TAKE CARE
OF MY PHYSICAL HEALTH AND WELL BEING.

ALL MY NEEDS ARE ALWAYS MET.

EVEN WHEN THE WORLD AROUND ME
FEELS CHAOTIC, I REMAIN ROOTED
FIRMLY TO THE GROUND.

& sometimes being human means that:

we get it wrong. we learn. we love. we lose. we love again. we feel all the feels. we struggle to understand our feelings. we care deeply. we feel lost. we find our way. we wish things were different yet we feel such gratitude. we have hard days. we get through them. **we find a way**.

JOURNAL

DATE / /

WRITE A FEW OF YOUR FAVORITE DAILY AFFIRMATIONS: I AM...
(E.G. I AM LOVED, I AM SAFE, I AM SUPPORTED BY MOTHER EARTH,
I AM BEAUTIFUL, I AM WORTHY OF ABUNDANCE IN ALL FORMS)

_____

_____

_____

_____

_____

GRATITUDE: WHAT ARE A FEW THINGS YOU ARE GRATEFUL FOR
TODAY?

_____

_____

_____

_____

WHAT CAN YOU DO TO GROUND YOURSELF TODAY? (E.G. A WALK
IN NATURE, A MEDITATION, WALKING BAREFOOT, OR A BREATH OR
TWO OF FRESH AIR— ANYTHING THAT WILL HELP YOU PAUSE AND
CONNECT WITH YOURSELF.)

_____

_____

_____

_____

_____

_____

_____

_____

_____

BREATHE IN

WRITING FLOW: TAKE THE SPACE BELOW TO WRITE WHATEVER
COMES THROUGH YOUR MIND. NO JUDGMENT, JUST ALLOWANCE...

_____
_____
_____
_____
_____
_____
_____
_____
_____
_____
_____
_____
_____
_____
_____
_____
_____
_____
_____
_____
_____
_____
_____
_____
_____

BREATHE OUT

JOURNAL

WRITE A FEW OF YOUR FAVORITE DAILY AFFIRMATIONS: I AM...

_____

_____

_____

_____

_____

GRATITUDE: WHAT ARE A FEW THINGS YOU ARE GRATEFUL FOR TODAY?

_____

_____

_____

_____

WHAT CAN YOU DO TO GROUND YOURSELF TODAY?

_____

_____

_____

_____

_____

_____

_____

_____

_____

_____

_____

BREATHE IN

WRITING FLOW: TAKE THE SPACE BELOW TO WRITE WHATEVER
COMES THROUGH YOUR MIND. NO JUDGMENT, JUST ALLOWANCE...

_____

_____

_____

_____

_____

_____

_____

_____

_____

_____

_____

_____

_____

_____

_____

_____

_____

_____

_____

_____

_____

_____

_____

_____

BREATHE OUT

JOURNAL

WRITE A FEW OF YOUR FAVORITE DAILY AFFIRMATIONS: I AM...

_____

_____

_____

_____

_____

GRATITUDE: WHAT ARE A FEW THINGS YOU ARE GRATEFUL FOR TODAY?

_____

_____

_____

_____

WHAT CAN YOU DO TO GROUND YOURSELF TODAY?

_____

_____

_____

_____

_____

_____

_____

_____

_____

_____

_____

BREATHE IN

WRITING FLOW: TAKE THE SPACE BELOW TO WRITE WHATEVER
COMES THROUGH YOUR MIND. NO JUDGMENT, JUST ALLOWANCE...

_____

_____

_____

_____

_____

_____

_____

_____

_____

_____

_____

_____

_____

_____

_____

_____

_____

_____

_____

_____

_____

_____

_____

_____

BREATHE OUT

JOURNAL

WRITE A FEW OF YOUR FAVORITE DAILY AFFIRMATIONS: I AM...

_____
_____
_____
_____
_____

GRATITUDE: WHAT ARE A FEW THINGS YOU ARE GRATEFUL FOR TODAY?

_____
_____
_____
_____

WHAT CAN YOU DO TO GROUND YOURSELF TODAY?

_____
_____
_____
_____
_____
_____
_____
_____
_____
_____
_____

BREATHE IN

WRITING FLOW: TAKE THE SPACE BELOW TO WRITE WHATEVER
COMES THROUGH YOUR MIND. NO JUDGMENT, JUST ALLOWANCE...

BREATHE OUT

JOURNAL

DATE / /

WRITE A FEW OF YOUR FAVORITE DAILY AFFIRMATIONS: I AM...

_____

_____

_____

_____

_____

GRATITUDE: WHAT ARE A FEW THINGS YOU ARE GRATEFUL FOR TODAY?

_____

_____

_____

_____

WHAT CAN YOU DO TO GROUND YOURSELF TODAY?

_____

_____

_____

_____

_____

_____

_____

_____

_____

_____

_____

_____

BREATHE IN

WRITING FLOW: TAKE THE SPACE BELOW TO WRITE WHATEVER
COMES THROUGH YOUR MIND. NO JUDGMENT, JUST ALLOWANCE...

_____

_____

_____

_____

_____

_____

_____

_____

_____

_____

_____

_____

_____

_____

_____

_____

_____

_____

_____

_____

_____

_____

_____

_____

_____

_____

BREATHE OUT

JOURNAL

WRITE A FEW OF YOUR FAVORITE DAILY AFFIRMATIONS: I AM...

_____

_____

_____

_____

_____

GRATITUDE: WHAT ARE A FEW THINGS YOU ARE GRATEFUL FOR TODAY?

_____

_____

_____

_____

WHAT CAN YOU DO TO GROUND YOURSELF TODAY?

_____

_____

_____

_____

_____

_____

_____

_____

_____

_____

_____

BREATHE IN

WRITING FLOW: TAKE THE SPACE BELOW TO WRITE WHATEVER
COMES THROUGH YOUR MIND. NO JUDGMENT, JUST ALLOWANCE...

_____
_____
_____
_____
_____
_____
_____
_____
_____
_____
_____
_____
_____
_____
_____
_____
_____
_____
_____
_____
_____
_____
_____

BREATHE OUT

JOURNAL

WRITE A FEW OF YOUR FAVORITE DAILY AFFIRMATIONS: I AM...

_____

_____

_____

_____

_____

GRATITUDE: WHAT ARE A FEW THINGS YOU ARE GRATEFUL FOR
TODAY?

_____

_____

_____

_____

WHAT CAN YOU DO TO GROUND YOURSELF TODAY?

_____

_____

_____

_____

_____

_____

_____

_____

_____

_____

_____

BREATHE IN

WRITING FLOW: TAKE THE SPACE BELOW TO WRITE WHATEVER
COMES THROUGH YOUR MIND. NO JUDGMENT, JUST ALLOWANCE...

_____

_____

_____

_____

_____

_____

_____

_____

_____

_____

_____

_____

_____

_____

_____

_____

_____

_____

_____

_____

_____

_____

_____

BREATHE OUT

JOURNAL

WRITE A FEW OF YOUR FAVORITE DAILY AFFIRMATIONS: I AM...

_____

_____

_____

_____

_____

GRATITUDE: WHAT ARE A FEW THINGS YOU ARE GRATEFUL FOR TODAY?

_____

_____

_____

_____

WHAT CAN YOU DO TO GROUND YOURSELF TODAY?

_____

_____

_____

_____

_____

_____

_____

_____

_____

_____

_____

_____

BREATHE IN

WRITING FLOW: TAKE THE SPACE BELOW TO WRITE WHATEVER
COMES THROUGH YOUR MIND. NO JUDGMENT, JUST ALLOWANCE...

_____

_____

_____

_____

_____

_____

_____

_____

_____

_____

_____

_____

_____

_____

_____

_____

_____

_____

_____

_____

_____

_____

_____

BREATHE OUT

JOURNAL

DATE / /

WRITE A FEW OF YOUR FAVORITE DAILY AFFIRMATIONS: I AM...

_____

_____

_____

_____

_____

GRATITUDE: WHAT ARE A FEW THINGS YOU ARE GRATEFUL FOR
TODAY?

_____

_____

_____

_____

WHAT CAN YOU DO TO GROUND YOURSELF TODAY?

_____

_____

_____

_____

_____

_____

_____

_____

_____

_____

_____

_____

BREATHE IN

WRITING FLOW: TAKE THE SPACE BELOW TO WRITE WHATEVER
COMES THROUGH YOUR MIND. NO JUDGMENT, JUST ALLOWANCE...

_____
_____
_____
_____
_____
_____
_____
_____
_____
_____
_____
_____
_____
_____
_____
_____
_____
_____
_____
_____
_____
_____
_____
_____
_____

BREATHE OUT

JOURNAL

WRITE A FEW OF YOUR FAVORITE DAILY AFFIRMATIONS: I AM...

_____

_____

_____

_____

_____

GRATITUDE: WHAT ARE A FEW THINGS YOU ARE GRATEFUL FOR TODAY?

_____

_____

_____

_____

WHAT CAN YOU DO TO GROUND YOURSELF TODAY?

_____

_____

_____

_____

_____

_____

_____

_____

_____

_____

_____

BREATHE IN

WRITING FLOW: TAKE THE SPACE BELOW TO WRITE WHATEVER
COMES THROUGH YOUR MIND. NO JUDGMENT, JUST ALLOWANCE...

_____

_____

_____

_____

_____

_____

_____

_____

_____

_____

_____

_____

_____

_____

_____

_____

_____

_____

_____

_____

_____

_____

_____

_____

BREATHE OUT

SECTION TWO:
Meeting Your Inner Child

MEETING YOUR INNER CHILD

"THE INNER CHILD LIVES WITHIN ALL OF US, IT'S THE PART OF US THAT FEELS EMOTIONS AND IS PLAYFUL, INTUITIVE, AND CREATIVE. USUALLY HIDDEN UNDER OUR GROWN-UP PERSONAS, THE INNER CHILD HOLDS THE KEY TO INTIMACY IN RELATIONSHIPS, PHYSICAL AND EMOTIONAL WELL BEING, RECOVERY FROM ADDICTIONS, AND THE CREATIVITY AND WISDOM OF OUR INNER SELVES."

— *Lucia Cappachione*

The inner child is seen as the part of us that holds our core wounds and unresolved emotional pain. These wounds can result from early childhood experiences such as humiliation, intimidation, neglect, abandonment, abuse, or other trauma. The inner child is also thought to represent the creative, playful, and imaginative aspects of ourselves that we may have suppressed or ignored as we grew older.

When we don't acknowledge or heal these wounds, we will continue to manifest the thoughts, feelings, and behaviors associated with them as adults. The inner child can also affect our ability to pursue our passions and live authentically, as we may have internalized beliefs or messages from our past that hold us back from expanding.

Beginning the process of healing our inner child involves acknowledging and accepting these past wounds and emotions, and providing a safe and nurturing environment to address and heal them. This reconnects us with our true essence and releases emotional pain that may have been holding us back.

By healing our inner child, we can reclaim our creativity, joy, authenticity, and live more fulfilling and meaningful lives. Unlocking our creativity is what brings color to the world; after all, what is life if not art? We're all artists, and we can all create in alignment with our hearts, but limiting beliefs and chakra blockages hold us back.

"The wound is not my fault, but the healing is my responsibility."

— *Denice Frohman*

JOURNAL

DAILY AFFIRMATIONS: I AM...

_____

_____

_____

_____

_____

GRATITUDE: WHAT ARE A FEW THINGS YOU ARE GRATEFUL FOR
TODAY?

_____

_____

_____

_____

HOW CAN YOU ADD PLAY INTO YOUR DAY? (E.G. CREATIVE
PRACTICE LIKE PAINTING, ART, OR AN ADDITION OF HUMOR
WHEREVER YOU CAN CREATE IT)

_____

_____

_____

_____

WHAT WORDS OF AFFIRMATION, SUPPORT, OR VALIDATION
CAN YOU GIVE YOUR INNER CHILD?

_____

_____

_____

_____

_____

_____

BREATHE IN

BREATHE OUT

REMEMBERING YOUR INNER CHILD

Kids don't care about being cool or what's "trendy." They're unashamedly themselves, and that is their magic. Let's channel some of that. Start writing a brief description of your inner child.

WHO ARE THEY?

_____

_____

_____

_____

WHAT DO THEY LIKE?

_____

_____

_____

_____

WHAT DO YOU WISH YOUR PARENTS KNEW ABOUT THEM?

_____

_____

_____

_____

WHAT ARE THEIR FAVORITE MOVIE CHARACTERS?

_____

_____

_____

IF YOU HAD THE OPPORTUNITY TO MEET YOUR INNER CHILD RIGHT NOW, WHAT WOULD YOU TELL THEM?

_____

_____

_____

IF THEY WERE A MYTHICAL CREATURE, WHO WOULD THEY BE (E.G. FAIRY, MERMAID, UNICORN, WITCH)?

_____

_____

_____

_____

_____

WHAT INSPIRES THEM (MAGIC, PIRATE ADVENTURE, CANDYLAND, TIME WITH THEIR FAMILY, MYSTERIOUS FAIRY FORESTS, NATURE)? ANYTHING GOES, JUST GET WRITING!

_____

_____

_____

_____

_____

_____

_____

_____

_____

_____

_____

Suggestion: Get a few close friends together and host a gathering themed around your answers. Encourage all to bring their weirdest inner child A-Game. This could be a costume party, a painting party, a scavenger hunt for pirate booty, an Alice in Wonderland tea party, anything. It's up to you. Make it as cool or uncool as you think your friends can handle.

JOURNAL

DAILY AFFIRMATIONS: I AM...

_____
_____
_____
_____
_____

GRATITUDE: WHAT ARE A FEW THINGS YOU ARE GRATEFUL FOR TODAY?

_____
_____
_____
_____

HOW CAN YOU ADD PLAY INTO YOUR DAY?

_____
_____
_____
_____

WHAT WORDS OF AFFIRMATION, SUPPORT, OR VALIDATION CAN YOU GIVE YOUR INNER CHILD?

_____
_____
_____
_____
_____
_____

BREATHE IN

WRITING FLOW: TAKE THE SPACE BELOW TO WRITE WHATEVER
COMES THROUGH YOUR MIND. NO JUDGMENT, JUST ALLOWANCE...

_____
_____
_____
_____
_____
_____
_____
_____
_____
_____
_____
_____
_____
_____
_____
_____
_____
_____
_____
_____
_____
_____
_____
_____

BREATHE OUT

TALKING TO YOUR INNER CHILD

Let's begin by saying hello to your 5-year-old self. If you have any photos of you at this age, it could help to take them out to remind you of who you were. For example, make your phone home screen a photo of you as a child for daily reminders that this version exists within you at all times.

- Begin by getting very clear on how you're going to talk to them from now on. They are precious and pure. A child of God, an innocent ball of energy. They have unlimited potential and creativity. Talk to them in a way that affirms they're completely worthy of anything their heart desires.
- Write them a letter below.

- If uncomfortable memories arise, hold them fiercely. Tell your inner child that you love them and that they are safe now. Apologize for any unconscious adult behavior that hurt them. It's important that they know and believe they are safe now.

_____

_____

_____

_____

_____

_____

_____

_____

_____

_____

_____

_____

_____

_____

Repeat this practice as often as you need and return to it whenever you feel shaky, unsafe, or uncomfortable. Internalize this new dialogue within yourself. This is your new **EMPOWERING** and **SUPPORTIVE** inner dialogue. This is how we talk to ourselves. **We are worthy**.

ADDITIONAL THINGS YOU CAN DO TO CONNECT WITH YOUR INNER CHILD:

When we connect to our inner child, we connect to our creativity. After all, children are the most creative beings with an untouched imagination of infinite possibilities and pure light. Think about the things you did as a kid.

This is a good way to remember being in this energy.

- Creative painting
- Jumping on a trampoline
- Flying a kite
- Building legos
- Running into the ocean

JOURNAL

DAILY AFFIRMATIONS: I AM...

_____
_____
_____
_____
_____

GRATITUDE: WHAT ARE A FEW THINGS YOU ARE GRATEFUL FOR
TODAY?

_____
_____
_____
_____

HOW CAN YOU ADD PLAY INTO YOUR DAY?

_____
_____
_____

WHAT WORDS OF AFFIRMATION, SUPPORT, OR VALIDATION CAN
YOU GIVE YOUR INNER CHILD?

_____
_____
_____
_____
_____
_____
_____

BREATHE IN

WRITING FLOW: TAKE THE SPACE BELOW TO WRITE WHATEVER
COMES THROUGH YOUR MIND. NO JUDGMENT, JUST ALLOWANCE...

_____

_____

_____

_____

_____

_____

_____

_____

_____

_____

_____

_____

_____

_____

_____

_____

_____

_____

_____

_____

_____

_____

_____

BREATHE OUT

SACRAL CHAKRA
EMOTIONAL, CREATIVE, AND SEXUAL EXPRESSION

ELEMENT: **WATER**
COLOR: **ORANGE**

The sacral chakra is the second chakra and the energy center for the vital force, or prana, located right below the navel. This energy rules emotions and assists in letting go, accepting change, and transformation in life. It is also a direct line to our creativity, intuition, and sexual pleasure.

When the sacral chakra is blocked or imbalanced, it can make you feel emotionally unstable. You will either be highly sensitive, or you will not be in touch with your emotions at all. You may be lacking creativity or discipline, as well as experiencing an addiction to sensory pleasure.

When the second chakra is open and activated, it enables us to shape our desires. As the center of passion, it awakens the power of creation. A person with an open and balanced sacral chakra has the ability to enjoy the senses with discipline and keep their emotions and relationships in balance.

PRACTICE & GUIDED MEDITATION
RELEASE TRAUMA AND BLOCKAGES

Trauma and negative past experiences get stored in our bodies and can block our energy from flowing to the upper chakras which are essential for bringing our manifestations into reality. For some, this can be a very challenging part of our evolution.

That's why there's the saying "the body keeps score". Yet this doesn't have to be your reality. Trauma, depending on the level, can be difficult to work through. However, it is the key to healing. Avoiding it will only cause it to grow internally where it could later manifest as illness and disease. Acknowledging, processing, and releasing it is your way out of suffering internally and externally— it is the key to freedom.

Take a deep breath, and know that the only way out, is in. Let's begin. We believe in you and remember that you believe in yourself too. This is the most important part of the equation.

GUIDED MEDITATION #3
SACRAL CHAKRA RELEASE & BALANCING

- Let's begin by sitting in a comfortable position in a private area or room, or outside in nature if you wish.
- Scan the QR Code above and follow it to the guided meditation or use a 417 hz Binaural Frequency via Spotify or Youtube.
- Begin with inhales and exhales as deeply as feels comfortable.
- Relax. Calm and clear your mind.
- Release any tension you may feel in your body.
- Move your awareness to your sacral chakra. It is located above your root chakra and below your navel.
- Imagine it as a bright orange ball of energy.
- Say hello to it, introduce yourself.
- Ask it: what is present?
- Begin to receive any information it is ready to show you.
- Deep breaths, in and out.
- Allow any past memories to come up. Try to simply observe these memories.
- Send your healing stream of energy down to it.
- Talk to your sacral chakra as your inner child. Tell it that it is safe. Acknowledge your feelings. Hold yourself with your energy. Give yourself permission to BE. Release any fear or uncomfortable emotions as you exhale.

JOURNAL PROMPTS

WHAT CAME UP FOR YOU DURING YOUR MEDITATION?

_____

_____

_____

_____

WERE THERE ANY PEOPLE THAT CAME TO MIND?

_____

_____

_____

_____

WAS THERE AN EMOTION/FEELING THAT STOOD OUT FOR YOU?
WHERE IN YOUR BODY DID YOU FEEL IT?

_____

_____

_____

_____

WERE THERE ANY MEMORIES THAT CAME UP?

_____

_____

_____

_____

WRITE YOUR INNER CHILD ANOTHER LETTER, EXPRESSING ALL THE
FEELINGS YOU HAVE AND WHAT YOU WOULD SAY TO THEM FROM
YOUR NEW AWARENESS AND PERSPECTIVE NOW. AFFIRM THAT IT'S
ALL GOING TO BE OK.

_____

_____

_____

_____

_____

_____

_____

_____

_____

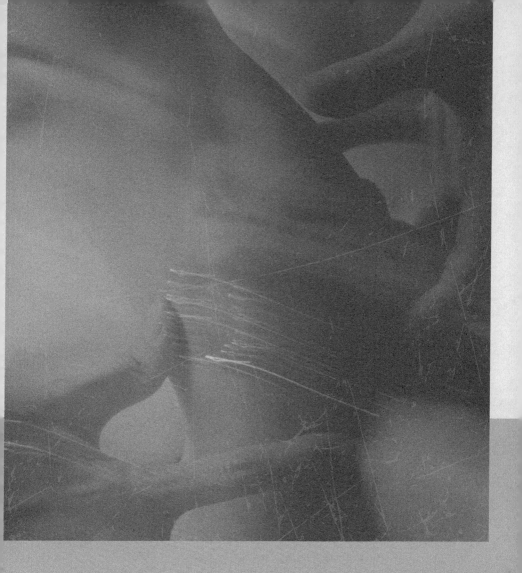

This is a practice that should be repeated for best results. Both the body and the mind have been observed to show resistance when processing trauma, which emphasizes the need for patience and persistence. Instead of revealing all aspects of your traumas at once, the body and mind tend to unveil the necessary information you need to receive gradually in perfect timing. Therefore, it is advisable to trust the body's natural process, as it will reveal what is needed when one is prepared to handle it.

Amazing job. We applaud you for your strength and valiance – this is not easy stuff.

JOURNAL

DATE / /

DAILY AFFIRMATIONS: I AM...

_____
_____
_____
_____
_____

GRATITUDE: WHAT ARE A FEW THINGS YOU ARE GRATEFUL FOR
TODAY?

_____
_____
_____
_____

HOW CAN YOU ADD PLAY INTO YOUR DAY?

_____
_____
_____
_____

WHAT WORDS OF AFFIRMATION, SUPPORT, OR VALIDATION CAN
YOU GIVE YOUR INNER CHILD?

_____
_____
_____
_____
_____
_____
_____

BREATHE IN

WRITING FLOW: TAKE THE SPACE BELOW TO WRITE WHATEVER
COMES THROUGH YOUR MIND. NO JUDGMENT, JUST ALLOWANCE...

BREATHE OUT

PRACTICE
INTUITIVE MOVEMENT

As you begin releasing trauma, it's important to move this energy through your body to fully release it. Practices like dance, yoga, pilates, boxing, and walks or runs in nature will help you process and release these experiences. They also stimulate creativity! Some of our favorite ideas have come to us during movement practices. The more you can allow the light to come in, the more the shadows will be transmuted into light.

Sacral Chakra Affirmations

I AM CREATIVE.

I AM SACRED.

I AM DIVINE FEMININE ENERGY.

I NOURISH HEALTHY BOUNDARIES.

I EXPERIENCE THE PRESENT MOMENT
THROUGH MY SENSES.

I AM PASSIONATE.

I FEEL PLEASURE AND ABUNDANCE WITH
EVERY BREATH I TAKE.

I VALUE AND RESPECT MY BODY.

I ALLOW MYSELF TO EXPERIENCE PLEASURE.

MY SEXUALITY IS SACRED.

I TREAT MY BODY AS A TEMPLE.

EMOTIONS ARE THE LANGUAGE OF MY SOUL.

I AM AT PEACE.

I LET MY INNER CHILD PLAY.

JOURNAL

DATE / /

DAILY AFFIRMATIONS: I AM...

_____
_____
_____
_____
_____

GRATITUDE: WHAT ARE A FEW THINGS YOU ARE GRATEFUL FOR TODAY?

_____
_____
_____
_____

HOW CAN YOU ADD PLAY INTO YOUR DAY?

_____
_____
_____

WHAT WORDS OF AFFIRMATION, SUPPORT, OR VALIDATION CAN YOU GIVE YOUR INNER CHILD?

_____
_____
_____
_____
_____
_____
_____

BREATHE IN

WRITING FLOW: TAKE THE SPACE BELOW TO WRITE WHATEVER
COMES THROUGH YOUR MIND. NO JUDGMENT, JUST ALLOWANCE...

BREATHE OUT

JOURNAL

DATE / /

DAILY AFFIRMATIONS: I AM...

_____
_____
_____
_____
_____

GRATITUDE: WHAT ARE A FEW THINGS YOU ARE GRATEFUL FOR
TODAY?

_____
_____
_____
_____

HOW CAN YOU ADD PLAY INTO YOUR DAY?

_____
_____
_____
_____

WHAT WORDS OF AFFIRMATION, SUPPORT, OR VALIDATION CAN
YOU GIVE YOUR INNER CHILD?

_____
_____
_____
_____
_____
_____
_____

BREATHE IN

WRITING FLOW: TAKE THE SPACE BELOW TO WRITE WHATEVER
COMES THROUGH YOUR MIND. NO JUDGMENT, JUST ALLOWANCE...

_____

_____

_____

_____

_____

_____

_____

_____

_____

_____

_____

_____

_____

_____

_____

_____

_____

_____

_____

_____

_____

BREATHE OUT

SECTION THREE:
Dancing With Your Shadow

What is Shadow Work?

"THE SHADOW IS NEEDED NOW MORE THAN EVER. WE HEAL THE WORLD WHEN WE HEAL OURSELVES, AND HOPE SHINES BRIGHTEST WHEN IT ILLUMINATES THE DARK."

– Sasha Graham

Shadow work is the process of delving into your unconscious mind to reveal and confront the aspects of yourself that are suppressed and concealed from your awareness. These suppressed aspects can include trauma or parts of yourself and your personality that you consider undesirable.

The purpose of shadow work is to discover all of the parts of yourself that have been abandoned, repressed, or rejected. Once these aspects of yourself are uncovered and brought to your awareness, you liberate yourself by cultivating unconditional love, compassion, and acceptance for ALL of yourself. It requires non judgemental awareness and complete acceptance of the body and the mind. Like mindfulness, shadow work is an approach to psychological healing that recognizes one's inner wisdom and ability to facilitate personal growth and expansion.

"Your life will be transformed when you make peace with your shadow. The caterpillar will become a breathtakingly beautiful butterfly. You will no longer have to pretend to be someone you're not. You will no longer have to prove you're good enough."

– Debbie Ford

One of the most potent energies you can transmute in this lifetime is **pain**. Learning to go into this emotion and turn it into power can make you unstoppable. Many of us run from it, after all why would we want to be uncomfortable? The problem that arises is this: unresolved pain is like an untreated wound, the longer it festers the worse it will get and the more damage it will do.

Owning your mistakes, whether you've been the perpetrator or the victim in your story, can be a super-value pack of wisdom that will not only help you reach new levels of strength, resilience, self-love and self-worth but when expressed can also inspire and offer value to others.

This is the part where giving yourself **grace, forgiveness, and permission to make mistakes** is essential. If during this section you feel overwhelmed we encourage you to reach out to a trusted friend, family member, or therapist for support. Just having someone to talk through this with can be immensely healing.

Participating in Shadow Work is the path of the warrior, ultimately leading to your role **as a leader**. Much of our shadow may be rooted in intergenerational trauma, the transferral of behavioral patterns and conditioning across generations within a family or community. This idea suggests that the psychological and emotional impact of traumatic events experienced by one generation can be passed down to succeeding generations. When we look within we have the opportunity to end these unconscious cycles with us and plant seeds for a new way forward.

As you embark on this leg of the journey we'd like to thank you on behalf of your ancestors and future generations.

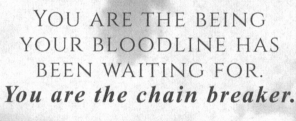

YOU ARE THE BEING
YOUR BLOODLINE HAS
BEEN WAITING FOR.
You are the chain breaker.

"SHADOW WORK IS THE PATH OF THE HEART WARRIOR." — *Carl Jung*

"YIN AND YANG, MALE AND FEMALE, STRONG AND WEAK, RIGID AND TENDER, HEAVEN AND EARTH, LIGHT AND DARKNESS, THUNDER AND LIGHTNING, COLD AND WARMTH, GOOD AND EVIL...THE INTERPLAY OF OPPOSITE PRINCIPLES CONSTITUTES THE UNIVERSE." — *Confucius*

"UNLESS YOU LEARN TO FACE YOUR OWN SHADOWS, YOU WILL CONTINUE TO SEE THEM IN OTHERS, BECAUSE THE WORLD OUTSIDE OF YOU IS ONLY A REFLECTION OF THE WORLD INSIDE OF YOU." — *The Minds Journal*

JOURNAL

DAILY AFFIRMATIONS: I AM...

_____
_____
_____
_____
_____

GRATITUDE: WHAT ARE A FEW THINGS YOU ARE GRATEFUL FOR TODAY?

_____
_____
_____
_____
_____

WHAT FEARS OR LIMITING BELIEFS CAN I FOCUS ON LETTING GO OF?

_____
_____
_____
_____

WHAT EMOTIONS AM I FEELING IN MY BODY RIGHT NOW?

_____
_____
_____
_____
_____
_____
_____

BREATHE IN

WHAT SELF−CARE PRACTICE CAN I RITUALIZE TODAY?

_____

_____

_____

_____

_____

WRITING FLOW: TAKE THE SPACE BELOW TO WRITE WHATEVER
COMES THROUGH YOUR MIND. NO JUDGMENT, JUST ALLOWANCE...

_____

_____

_____

_____

_____

_____

_____

_____

_____

_____

_____

_____

_____

_____

_____

BREATHE OUT

"YOUR SHADOW IS ALL OF THE THINGS, 'POSITIVE' AND
'NEGATIVE,' THAT YOU'VE DENIED ABOUT YOURSELF AND
HIDDEN BENEATH THE SURFACE OF THE MASK YOU FORGOT
THAT YOU'RE WEARING."

— *Oli Anderson*

Solar Plexus Chakra

ELEMENT: **FIRE**
COLOR: **YELLOW**

So you may be wondering, how does the solar plexus chakra tie into shadow work?

The solar plexus chakra is the third chakra located four fingerbreadths above the navel, just below the rib cage. This is the energy center that rules personal power, self-esteem, and confidence.

When the third chakra is in balance, you will feel confident, self-motivated, and have a sense of purpose. When surrounded by negative energy, you can suffer from low self-esteem and have control issues.

The gift of the solar plexus is self acceptance, which is a key component in shadow work. When you begin to acknowledge and accept ALL parts of yourself, even the aspects that you have been programmed to believe are "undesirable", you are on the right path to bringing your solar plexus back into balance.

By working with this energy center and intentionally cultivating self love and acceptance, you begin to surrender shame and judgment, and return to a state of wholeness, confidence, and empowerment in who you are.

Practice & Guided Meditation
Self-Limiting Belief Cloud Bursting

Our beliefs create our realities.

Now, let's start manifesting. It's time to bring our highest potential into reality.

In this practice, you're going to focus on something that you want to create. Perhaps it's financial freedom or love. It is important that we clear self-limiting beliefs so that we unlock the doors to the infinite flow of the Universe's abundance and prosperity.

GUIDED MEDITATION #4
SELF-LIMITING BELIEF CLOUDBURSTING

- Let's begin by sitting in a comfortable position in a private area or room, or outside in nature if you wish.
- Scan the QR Code to the guided meditation above or use a 528 hz Binaural Frequency via Spotify or Youtube.
- Calm your mind by taking in some big inhales and exhales.
- Now visualize your dream, whether it's money to build your dream home or a future with your soulmate. What would it look like? Remember you can have ANYTHING - all possibilities exist in this universe.
- What will most likely happen is you are able to visualize this reality but will feel it to be an impossible feat, or "just a dream". When you feel this disconnect, begin to look with your awareness for the limiting beliefs keeping you from that reality.
- Become your awareness right now. Ask yourself, why? Why can't I have this dream? Why do I feel this is impossible? Why not me? Do not give up until you have an answer. Perhaps an internalized belief that you are unlovable or unworthy will arise. Go deeper.

- Why do you think that? Who told you that? Can you identify with your awareness a past trauma, perhaps during childhood, that created this self-limiting belief? This may bring up grief. So grieve, cry, scream, do whatever you need to release, but do not harm yourself or anyone else.
- Breathe in, breathe out, let it go.
- With your awareness, begin to look for where this self-limiting belief lives in your body (clue: do you feel a sensation in your body? Is there any tension in your internal landscape?). Direct your awareness to that part of your body.
- It's time to CloudBurst!!
- With your loving awareness, as gently as possible, begin to dissolve this belief. Visualize the negative belief as a cloud that is blocking light from both shining outward and entering. Feel the tension begin to dissolve in this area. There will be different layers to this feeling. Work with your awareness to dissolve it little by little. You are healing yourself and creating more space to allow light and abundance to flow through you.

Practice this again and again until that dream you visualized at the beginning not only feels realistic, but you know that it is going to happen. It's inevitable.

JOURNAL

DAILY AFFIRMATIONS: I AM...

_____

_____

_____

_____

_____

GRATITUDE: WHAT ARE A FEW THINGS YOU ARE GRATEFUL FOR TODAY?

_____

_____

_____

_____

_____

WHAT FEARS OR LIMITING BELIEFS CAN I FOCUS ON LETTING GO OF?

_____

_____

_____

_____

WHAT EMOTIONS AM I FEELING IN MY BODY RIGHT NOW?

_____

_____

_____

_____

_____

_____

_____

BREATHE IN

WHAT SELF–CARE PRACTICE CAN I RITUALIZE TODAY?

_____
_____
_____
_____
_____

WRITING FLOW: TAKE THE SPACE BELOW TO WRITE WHATEVER
COMES THROUGH YOUR MIND. NO JUDGMENT, JUST ALLOWANCE...

_____
_____
_____
_____
_____
_____
_____
_____
_____
_____
_____
_____
_____
_____
_____
_____
_____

BREATHE OUT

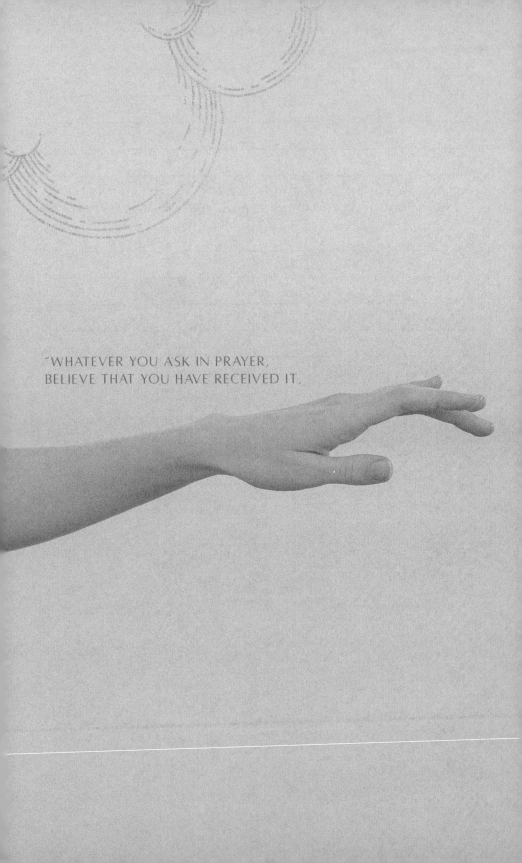

"WHATEVER YOU ASK IN PRAYER,
BELIEVE THAT YOU HAVE RECEIVED IT,

AND IT WILL BE YOURS."

— *Eckhart Tolle*

Defining Your Needs in Relationships

Whether you're single or in a relationship, defining and redefining our needs in relationships will help us to deepen our connections and attract what most authentically fulfills us.

In your world, you are the Queen of your realm, and you direct the universe as such. If the universe sends you a package that isn't quite right, send it back. Tell the universe to try again until it gets your order right. As you go through relationships that aren't quite right for you, as uncomfortable as these situations can be, you will learn valuable information about what your needs truly are underneath all the glitz and glam packaging. Having a nice car, a big house, and wearing nice clothes can be very attractive, but since those things are all material, it will not fulfill your soul.

Remember, you cannot attract what you haven't become. For example, if you value honesty you cannot expect to attract someone honest if you are being dishonest. So as you define your values, you must practice embodying them yourself.

Our Lover's List

BELOW LIST 10 QUALITIES YOU VALUE IN A PARTNER. YOU GET UNLIMITED REVISIONS AND ADDITIONS, SO RETURN TO THIS PAGE PERIODICALLY AND SEE IF THERE ARE ANY CHANGES YOU'D LIKE TO MAKE.

_____

_____

_____

_____

_____

_____

_____

_____

_____

_____

NOW VISUALIZE YOUR FUTURE PARTNER. DON'T GET TOO CAUGHT UP
ON HOW THEY WILL LOOK; THINK MORE ABOUT HOW YOU WILL FEEL
WITH THEM.

_____

_____

_____

_____

_____

_____

_____

_____

_____

_____

_____

_____

_____

_____

_____

_____

_____

_____

_____

_____

_____

_____

_____

WRITE OUT EVERYTHING THAT YOU WANT AND BE BRUTALLY HONEST
WITH YOURSELF. DESCRIBE THE RELATIONSHIP IN DETAIL. HOW WILL IT
FEEL? TELL THE UNIVERSE DIRECTLY THAT THIS IS WHAT YOU WANT.

JOURNAL

DAILY AFFIRMATIONS: I AM...

_____

_____

_____

_____

_____

GRATITUDE: WHAT ARE A FEW THINGS YOU ARE GRATEFUL FOR TODAY?

_____

_____

_____

_____

_____

WHAT FEARS OR LIMITING BELIEFS CAN I FOCUS ON LETTING GO OF?

_____

_____

_____

_____

WHAT EMOTIONS AM I FEELING IN MY BODY RIGHT NOW?

_____

_____

_____

_____

_____

_____

_____

BREATHE IN

WHAT SELF–CARE PRACTICE CAN I RITUALIZE TODAY?

_____

_____

_____

_____

_____

WRITING FLOW: TAKE THE SPACE BELOW TO WRITE WHATEVER
COMES THROUGH YOUR MIND. NO JUDGMENT, JUST ALLOWANCE...

_____

_____

_____

_____

_____

_____

_____

_____

_____

_____

_____

_____

_____

_____

_____

_____

_____

BREATHE OUT

SOLAR PLEXUS CHAKRA AFFIRMATIONS

I LOVE AND ACCEPT MYSELF FULLY.

I AM WORTHY OF ALL THE
WONDERFUL THINGS I DESIRE.

I CONFIDENTLY SHARE MY VALUE AND MY GIFTS.

I COURAGEOUSLY SHINE MY UNIQUE LIGHT.

I AM FREE AND JOYFUL.

I AM AT HOME IN MYSELF.

I AM LOVE AND SPIRIT.

I AM THE JEWEL AT THE CENTER OF THE LOTUS.

I AM RESPONSIBLE FOR ALL DECISION
I MAKE IN MY LIFE.

I BELIEVE IN MYSELF.

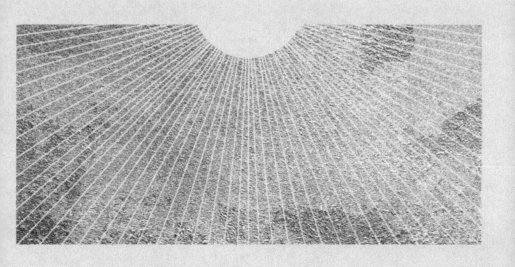

JOURNAL

DATE / /

DAILY AFFIRMATIONS: I AM...

_____
_____
_____
_____
_____

GRATITUDE: WHAT ARE A FEW THINGS YOU ARE GRATEFUL FOR TODAY?

_____
_____
_____
_____
_____

WHAT FEARS OR LIMITING BELIEFS CAN I FOCUS ON LETTING GO OF?

_____
_____
_____
_____

WHAT EMOTIONS AM I FEELING IN MY BODY RIGHT NOW?

_____
_____
_____
_____
_____
_____

BREATHE IN

WHAT SELF-CARE PRACTICE CAN I RITUALIZE TODAY?

_____
_____
_____
_____
_____

WRITING FLOW: TAKE THE SPACE BELOW TO WRITE WHATEVER
COMES THROUGH YOUR MIND. NO JUDGMENT, JUST ALLOWANCE...

_____
_____
_____
_____
_____
_____

_____
_____
_____
_____
_____
_____
_____
_____
_____
_____
_____

BREATHE OUT

Psychedelic Plant Medicines

The psychedelic experience has been a part of human history for thousands of years. Many cultures around the world still use these substances in ceremonial settings for healing, divine inspiration, and a way to connect to Source/God/Universe. We are now finally seeing the scientific and medical community acknowledge the positive effects these medicines can have on a person's mental health, particularly those dealing with anxiety, depression, and addiction.

In terms of shadow work, these mind-expanding molecules have been a highly impactful part of our own personal journeys. It is our view that **careful and conscious** psychedelic use can be one of the most effective modalities of transformation in the least amount of time. A single full-dose experience of psilocybin (magic mushrooms) can produce lasting effects that even six months of talk therapy can barely achieve.

Understanding Their Role In Relationship To Us

Imagine you are born with a special pair of glasses. These glasses allow you to only see a small fraction of the reality right in front of you. While you aren't aware that you are wearing these glasses (because how could you-- you were born with them) inside of your being, you "know" this isn't all there is.

While it used to be religion that sufficed as a remedy to satiate this inner "knowing", we are moving into a new paradigm where the middle man that was previously believed to be needed for spiritual/divine experience is no longer required. What psychedelics do is take these glasses off and allow you to see a much wider view of your reality and simultaneously allow you direct access to the divine. No religious leader, priest, or "holy man" is needed.

This can be absolutely amazing for those feeling stuck, disempowered, or if their life just feels generally lackluster. However, let us be very clear that these medicines must be handled with intention, mindfulness, and care. A guide or facilitator to hold space while you journey is highly recommended for higher doses.

For lower doses though, we want to empower you to feel safe and comfortable should you decide to embark on a self-guided solo journey. With a little mindset preparation and a whole lot of nature, you can have an amazing journey needing little else than this journal.

"BUT ALONG WITH THE FEELING OF INEFFABILITY, THE CONVICTION THAT SOME PROFOUND OBJECTIVE TRUTH HAS BEEN DISCLOSED TO YOU IS A HALLMARK OF THE MYSTICAL EXPERIENCE, REGARDLESS OF WHETHER IT HAS BEEN OCCASIONED BY A DRUG, MEDITATION, FASTING, FLAGELLATION, OR SENSORY DEPRIVATION.

WILLIAM JAMES GAVE A NAME TO THIS CONVICTION: THE NOETIC QUALITY. PEOPLE FEEL THEY HAVE BEEN LET IN ON A DEEP SECRET OF THE UNIVERSE, AND THEY CANNOT BE SHAKEN FROM THAT CONVICTION."

— *Michael Pollan*

SELF-GUIDED JOURNEY
(CAN BE SOLO OR WITH A TRUSTED FRIEND)

How to Prepare:
- Prepare for your trip in advance.
- Pack like you are taking yourself on a picnic in your favorite park and make sure to check the weather – if there is rain or snow expected, pick a different day.

Checklist:
- ☐ Water
- ☐ Music
- ☐ Snacks
- ☐ Headphones
- ☐ Blanket/towel

Before embarking, do a mindset check! Are you in a stable and generally positive place mentally? If you are dealing with fresh trauma such as a loss of a loved one or pet, suicidal thoughts or actions, or any volatile recent events, hold off until you've secured a facilitator to guide you on your journey. But if you are in an exploratory and adventurous spirit, let's go. Curiosity is your best friend on this trip so embrace it fully.

Start by repeating some positive affirmations to yourself and bringing to mind things you are grateful for.

Listen to some of your favorite feel-good songs or Ram Dass - Sit around the Fire to ease you into the experience.

As you journey, if uncomfortable feelings arise you can write them here. If feelings of fear come up, always, always remember to **SURRENDER**. This will be your mantra; don't fight the medicine, surrender to it and breathe. Trust that the intelligence of the mushroom knows where to go and what to show you.

During any uncomfortable periods that may arise, the act of connecting with the Earth can be very helpful. Reach out a hand and feel her energy. You are safe, you are held by Mama Gaia.

Things NOT to Do:
- Do NOT drink alcohol or climb up walls/buildings

JOURNEY NOTES

DATE / /

POST JOURNEY REFLECTION

- How was your experience?
- What did you feel?
- What did you see?
- Did you learn anything? About yourself, about the world?
- Write a short summary of your experience. No judgment, just allowance.

JOURNAL

DAILY AFFIRMATIONS: I AM...

_____

_____

_____

_____

_____

GRATITUDE: WHAT ARE A FEW THINGS YOU ARE GRATEFUL FOR
TODAY?

_____

_____

_____

_____

_____

WHAT FEARS OR LIMITING BELIEFS CAN I FOCUS ON LETTING GO OF?

_____

_____

_____

WHAT EMOTIONS AM I FEELING IN MY BODY RIGHT NOW?

_____

_____

_____

_____

_____

_____

BREATHE IN

WHAT SELF-CARE PRACTICE CAN I RITUALIZE TODAY?

_____

_____

_____

_____

_____

WRITING FLOW: TAKE THE SPACE BELOW TO WRITE WHATEVER
COMES THROUGH YOUR MIND. NO JUDGMENT, JUST ALLOWANCE...

_____

_____

_____

_____

_____

_____

_____

_____

_____

_____

_____

_____

_____

_____

_____

_____

BREATHE OUT

RITUALIZE YOUR LIFE

The ancients used rituals in daily life to strengthen their relationship with self and honor their connection with the Divine. Today we call these sacred practices self-care. We are not here to only serve others; it's important we set aside sacred time to honor ourselves.

Soaking in herbal infused bath salts can be amazing for clearing energy picked up from others (especially good for empaths) and releasing anything no longer serving us. Burning sacred herbs and plants such as sage, sandalwood, lotus flower, and paolo santo have been used for centuries for spiritual purification and ascending lower states of consciousness. Timing these practices with the phases of the moon and setting intentions for what you'd like to create can bring even more transformational energy into your life.

PRACTICE
RITUAL CREATION

BELOW, CREATE YOUR OWN RITUAL. START BY IDENTIFYING WHAT MAKES YOU FEEL GOOD, BEAUTIFUL, SENSUAL, LOVED, CONNECTED, AND SO FORTH.. THIS COULD BE CRYSTALS, CANDLES, ESSENTIAL OILS, INCENSE, MUSIC, DANCING, HERBAL TEAS, TAROT CARDS, SACRED ITEMS THAT HAVE SPECIAL MEANING TO YOU.

_____

_____

_____

_____

_____

_____

_____

_____

_____

_____

_____

HOW CAN YOU RITUALIZE THESE THINGS TO BRING YOU PEACE, CLARITY, AND CONNECTEDNESS WITHIN YOURSELF?

_____

_____

_____

_____

_____

IF YOU WERE A GODDESS (WHICH YOU ARE WINK, WINK) HOW WOULD YOU CONNECT WITH THE DIVINE? WHAT DOES DIVINE MEAN TO YOU? YOU GET TO DECIDE.

_____

_____

_____

_____

_____

_____

_____

_____

_____

_____

_____

_____

_____

_____

_____

_____

JOURNAL

DATE / /

DAILY AFFIRMATIONS: I AM...

_____

_____

_____

_____

_____

GRATITUDE: WHAT ARE A FEW THINGS YOU ARE GRATEFUL FOR TODAY?

_____

_____

_____

_____

_____

WHAT FEARS OR LIMITING BELIEFS CAN I FOCUS ON LETTING GO OF?

_____

_____

_____

_____

WHAT EMOTIONS AM I FEELING IN MY BODY RIGHT NOW?

_____

_____

_____

_____

_____

_____

BREATHE IN

WHAT SELF–CARE PRACTICE CAN I RITUALIZE TODAY?

_____

_____

_____

_____

_____

WRITING FLOW: TAKE THE SPACE BELOW TO WRITE WHATEVER
COMES THROUGH YOUR MIND. NO JUDGMENT, JUST ALLOWANCE...

_____

_____

_____

_____

_____

_____

_____

_____

_____

_____

_____

_____

_____

_____

_____

BREATHE OUT

THEY ARE SCARED OF
WOMEN LIKE YOU.

WOMEN WITH HEARTS
BIG ENOUGH TO HOUSE
SUITCASES FULL OF PAIN.

WOMEN WITH LAUGHS
SO THERAPEUTIC THEY
CAN HEAL WOUNDS.

WOMEN WITH PASSION
FIERCE ENOUGH TO
START WILDFIRES.

THEY ARE SCARED OF
WHAT THEY CAN'T TAME
OR UNDERSTAND.

— *Billy Chapata*

Opening The Heart

Let's begin this section by connecting to our heart. The heart chakra deserves special attention as it is one of the most powerful keys to transformation. Many of us have been hurt — in some cases, many times over and over again. We may have subconsciously disconnected from our heart space. Remember that your reality is a reflection of what is going on within, whether you are aware of it or not. If you are broken hearted over something that happened in the past, you will continue to manifest this over and over again in different forms.

Heart Chakra

ELEMENT: **AIR**
COLOR: **GREEN**

Located in the middle of our chest, the heart chakra (fourth chakra) is the doorway to our inner temple, our soul, the infinite part of ourselves and is where our most powerful magnetic energy is generated.

It is the bridge between the lower and upper chakras, balancing the material and spiritual worlds and facilitating our emotional and physical well-being. Pure love opens the fourth chakra, allowing us to receive and give love unconditionally.

When there is an imbalance or block in the energy flow of the heart chakra, we may experience emotions of solitude, seclusion, and difficulty establishing connections with ourselves and people around us. This can result in challenges regarding trust and openness in expressing personal sentiments to others.

A balanced heart chakra brings love, compassion, and joy, fostering a deep connection with ourselves and the world. It opens us to life's experiences, enabling challenges to flow and resolve effortlessly. It unveils the beauty and love that surrounds us, allowing us to cultivate genuine connections with ourselves, loved ones, and nature.

The sacred medicinal cacao plant has been used in healing ceremonies by the Aztecs, Mayans, and other ancient cultures for millenia. It contains a molecule called theobromine that stimulates blood flow to the heart, which is why it's commonly known as the heart opener. We love ritualizing this practice and creating a safe space to connect with our inner circle.

Benefits of Cacao:
- Heart opening
- Improves brain function
- Mood boosting
- Increases focus
- High in antioxidants, magnesium, iron, calcium, and more
- Aphrodisiac

Cacao Ceremony:

\+ Start by getting your hands on some cacao-many natural food stores carry organic, high-quality cacao that we can't get enough of, or you can purchase some online, either powdered or chunk form will work.

\+ Create a delicious cacao beverage by following the recipe below.

Recipe:

- 1.5 cups of your preferred milk (nut, oat, whole, almond or soy).
- 1/4 cup of grated, chopped, or powdered cacao.
- 2 tbsp (or just sweeten to taste) of your preferred sweetener (coconut sugar or raw honey are our favorite)
- Warm the milk (don't boil) and slowly add your cacao until melted. You can also blend in a blender or mixer for extra froth. Add your sweetener and you're ready to indulge!

GUIDED MEDITATION #5
CONNECTING WITH YOUR HEART

- Get comfy and follow the QR Code above or find a 639 hz frequency (the frequency of the heart) via Spotify or Youtube.
- Enjoy your sacred cacao. Set an intention and bless it with love and gratitude.
- Let's begin by getting into a comfortable position- it's time to go inward. Start by taking some deep inhales and exhales.
- Calm and clear your mind.
- Move your awareness to your heart chakra located in the center of your chest. Imagine it as a powerful ball of green energy.
- Feel what is present.
- Begin to receive any information as it is ready to be shown to you.
- Deep breaths, in and out. Try to simply observe this information.
- Allow any discomfort or emotions you're feeling to come up.
- Breathe and release; tears are not only accepted but welcome.
- Send your healing stream of energy to your heart.
- Hold it with your hands.
- Watch its green glow become brighter and brighter as dark energy is exhaled.
- Talk to your heart chakra. Tell it you are sorry for any pain that it has held.
- Acknowledge its strength and give it compassion. It's time to share your light with the world so you can attract all that you wish for.

Journal about your experience.

Reflect on your experience and write out what is present for you. Release any judgment, shame, or guilt that you may be holding on to.

- How do you feel? Did you feel any sensations in the heart?
- Were there any people that came to mind?
- Did any memories come to the surface?
- Write yourself a note of gratitude, appreciation, encouragement, and love. You're doing great work.

JOURNAL

DATE / /

DAILY AFFIRMATIONS: I AM...

_____

_____

_____

_____

_____

GRATITUDE: WHAT ARE A FEW THINGS YOU ARE GRATEFUL FOR TODAY?

_____

_____

_____

_____

SELF–LOVE: WHAT DO I LOVE ABOUT MYSELF?

_____

_____

_____

_____

HOW CAN I SHOW COMPASSION TO MYSELF TODAY? HOW CAN I EXTEND THIS COMPASSION TO OTHERS?

_____

_____

_____

_____

_____

_____

_____

BREATHE IN

WRITING FLOW: TAKE THE SPACE BELOW TO WRITE WHATEVER
COMES THROUGH YOUR MIND. NO JUDGMENT, JUST ALLOWANCE...

BREATHE OUT

GIVING IS YOUR GREATEST GIFT

YOU GET WHAT YOU GIVE.

While this mantra has transactional undertones, there is a golden nugget of wisdom in the underlying principle.

When we open our hearts and give love unconditionally, the Universe will mirror this energy back at us. Where we all get tripped up is the attachment we have to who will reflect this love back to us and how we will receive it.

Many times, rejection shuts us down from receiving and giving the unconditional and infinite love that we all have the ability to generate. Trust that when your intentions in giving are pure, you will have this purity reflected back to you. It may not come from who you were expecting, but trust that you will receive the good you've put out.

Boundaries here are important though. We are by no means saying keep putting your precious energy into someone not returning it. We are simply saying don't internalize the sting of rejection. Feel it, release it, and keep on moving. Believe, believe, believe.

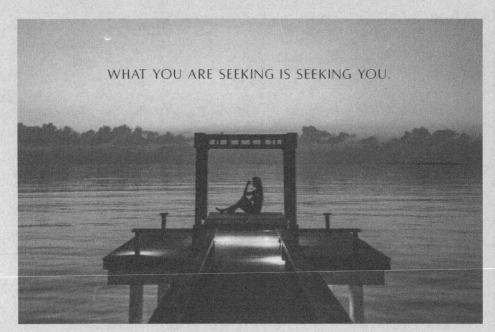

WHAT YOU ARE SEEKING IS SEEKING YOU.

JOURNAL

DAILY AFFIRMATIONS: I AM...

_____

_____

_____

_____

_____

GRATITUDE: WHAT ARE A FEW THINGS YOU ARE GRATEFUL FOR TODAY?

_____

_____

_____

_____

SELF—LOVE: WHAT DO I LOVE ABOUT MYSELF?

_____

_____

_____

HOW CAN I SHOW COMPASSION TO MYSELF TODAY? HOW CAN I EXTEND THIS COMPASSION TO OTHERS?

_____

_____

_____

_____

_____

_____

_____

WRITING FLOW: TAKE THE SPACE BELOW TO WRITE WHATEVER
COMES THROUGH YOUR MIND. NO JUDGMENT, JUST ALLOWANCE...

Heart Chakra Affirmations

I AM LOVE.

ALL BEINGS ARE MADE OF LOVE.

SPIRIT/DIVINITY RESIDES IN ME.

I AM OPEN TO GIVING AND RECEIVING LOVE.

MY HEART IS WHOLE.

I AM LOVED.

I AM GRATEFUL.

I FORGIVE MYSELF AND OTHERS.

I AM PEACEFUL.

JOURNAL

DATE / /

DAILY AFFIRMATIONS: I AM...

_____
_____
_____
_____
_____

GRATITUDE: WHAT ARE A FEW THINGS YOU ARE GRATEFUL FOR TODAY?

_____
_____
_____
_____

SELF-LOVE: WHAT DO I LOVE ABOUT MYSELF?

_____
_____
_____
_____

HOW CAN I SHOW COMPASSION TO MYSELF TODAY? HOW CAN I EXTEND THIS COMPASSION TO OTHERS?

_____
_____
_____
_____
_____
_____
_____

BREATHE IN

WRITING FLOW: TAKE THE SPACE BELOW TO WRITE WHATEVER
COMES THROUGH YOUR MIND. NO JUDGMENT, JUST ALLOWANCE...

_____

_____

_____

_____

_____

_____

_____

_____

_____

_____

_____

_____

_____

_____

_____

_____

_____

_____

_____

_____

_____

_____

BREATHE OUT

SECTION FOUR:
Manifesting Your Dreams

Manifesting Your Dreams

You've made it through the tough parts of facing your shadows and transmuting your limiting beliefs into ones that are empowering and expansive. Now you get to create your dream reality from a grounded space of connection to your heart, intuition, and soul's desires.

A few guiding principles as you begin manifesting:

- Write your desires as if you already have them. For example if you want to start a business, say "**I AM** an Entrepreneur", or if a new home is your wish, confidently state "**I HAVE** a new home". Claim it and you will become it.
- Thank the universe as if you've already received it. The Universe rewards gratitude. Try your best to embody the feeling of your desired reality being granted to you. Living in this mindset and feeling it as much as possible in your body will increase your desire's magnetism and speed up the manifestation process.
- Stay consistent. Remain loyal to the reality that you've claimed. When obstacles arise, remember who you are and do not doubt yourself. Believe it is already yours and it's only a matter of time until it makes its way to you.
- Repetition is key. Forming a new belief is mastered through the repetition of claiming and feeling a new set of thoughts. Don't be afraid to repeat yourself.

Practice
Abundance Mindset

Let's talk a bit about this. What does it mean when we use this phrase?

When we live in abundance, we recognize the interconnectedness of all beings and the infinite possibilities available to us. We begin to see that the Universe is abundant in its resources, opportunities, and possibilities, and that we can tap into this abundance by aligning ourselves with the Universe's natural flow of energy.

Reflect on these questions...

- Imagine the version of yourself that is financially free and living the life of your dreams. What would it look like to you? What clothes would you be wearing, what jewelry? Imagine an upgraded version of yourself now and really go into the fine details.
- What does luxury mean to you? Do you like decadent fragrances, nice wine, beautiful clothes, or a dream home? You decide.
- How do you feel? What does this upgraded energy you exude feel like? Feel it in your body now.

Remember that you deserve the life of your dreams, not solely because of how hard you work, not solely because of your special skills, but because you are infinitely abundant for just existing. You are worthy. Keep affirming this until it becomes a part of your belief system.

Our society doesn't encourage or embody this mindset because, as a collective, we operate out of fear and scarcity. But when we individually begin to shift our beliefs, we will begin to shift from the old paradigm of being to a new paradigm of sovereignty, abundance, and prosperity.

We recommend doing the practice above once daily with an 888hz frequency to accompany (the frequency of abundance). Money is just energy; align yours with it.

_____

_____

_____

_____

_____

_____

_____

_____

_____

_____

_____

JOURNAL

DATE / /

DAILY AFFIRMATIONS: I AM...

_____
_____
_____
_____
_____

WHAT AM I READY TO CREATE?

_____
_____
_____
_____
_____

VISUALIZE YOUR IDEAL REALITY AND DESCRIBE IT IN DETAIL:

_____
_____
_____
_____
_____
_____
_____
_____
_____
_____
_____

BREATHE IN

GRATITUDE: THANK THE UNIVERSE FOR GRANTING YOU...

_____

_____

_____

_____

WHAT ACTIONS CAN I TAKE TODAY TO CREATE MY DREAM
REALITY?

_____

_____

_____

_____

HOW DOES THIS NEW REALITY FEEL IN MY BODY?

_____

_____

_____

_____

_____

_____

_____

_____

_____

_____

_____

_____

BREATHE OUT

WRITING FLOW: TAKE THE SPACE BELOW TO WRITE WHATEVER
COMES THROUGH YOUR MIND. NO JUDGMENT, JUST ALLOWANCE...

"ACT ON YOUR EXCITEMENT TO THE BEST OF YOUR ABILITY WITH ZERO INSISTENCE ON THE OUTCOME, TRUSTING THAT YOUR HIGHER MIND WILL MANIFEST WHAT YOU TRULY NEED. AND THEN, WHATEVER MANIFESTS, KNOW THAT: THAT'S WHAT SERVES YOU IN THE BEST POSSIBLE WAY."

— *Bashar*

When we operate from a place of love and joy, our excitement is the primary key to the emergence of our desires. You have the ability to act on your joy about absolutely anything. Yet the problem for many of us is that our logical minds get in the way, and we don't believe that our highest joy is actually the most aligned path there is.

"Finding your passion" may seem daunting, but it starts really small. Begin to notice the things that spark your interest – what you feel drawn to and the activities that excite and bring you joy.

"If the things that are aligned with that beacon aren't reaching you, it's not because 'you're not vibrating at the resonance that you need to attract it'. It's because your definitions and beliefs are holding it away. So the true Secret of the Law of Attraction is not "how to learn to attract what you prefer", it's how to learn to let go of what you don't, so that you can let in what is trying to get to you automatically - by definition."

— *Bashar*

Journal about your interests below.

- What areas of life naturally draw your attention? Don't worry about anything but getting familiar with your natural interests/talents.
- What situations naturally fill you up with excitement and satisfaction? Examples could be sharing something new that you know will be helpful to your friends, making people laugh, being a part of a community, helping others in some way, connecting with nature. When do you truly feel the happiest and most satisfied?

You don't have to and most likely won't have all the answers right now, but as you start thinking about what naturally drives you, your vision and path will begin to unfold.

How can you create space in your life to follow your highest excitement regularly?

JOURNAL

DAILY AFFIRMATIONS: I AM...

_____
_____
_____
_____
_____

WHAT AM I READY TO CREATE?

_____
_____
_____
_____
_____

VISUALIZE YOUR IDEAL REALITY AND DESCRIBE IT IN DETAIL:

_____
_____
_____
_____
_____
_____
_____
_____
_____
_____
_____
_____

BREATHE IN

GRATITUDE: THANK THE UNIVERSE FOR GRANTING YOU...

_____

_____

_____

_____

WHAT ACTIONS CAN I TAKE TODAY TO CREATE MY DREAM
REALITY?

_____

_____

_____

HOW DOES THIS NEW REALITY FEEL IN MY BODY?

_____

_____

_____

_____

_____

_____

_____

_____

_____

_____

_____

_____

_____

_____

BREATHE OUT

WRITING FLOW: TAKE THE SPACE BELOW TO WRITE WHATEVER
COMES THROUGH YOUR MIND. NO JUDGMENT, JUST ALLOWANCE...

THROAT CHAKRA

ELEMENT: **SPACE, ETHER (AKASHA)**
COLOR: **BLUE**

The throat chakra is the fifth chakra, located at the base of the throat area. It governs self-expression, communication, and the ability to speak one's truth. It is your divine right as a human being to speak and be heard, and the purpose of the throat chakra is to communicate your needs, boundaries, and desires.

When our throat chakra holds blockages, communication breaks down which can manifest in difficulties expressing ourselves, being imaginative, trusting our inner voice, and connecting on a deeper level with ourselves and others.

A balanced throat chakra helps with internal and external communication and creative ideas. As the throat chakra opens, people often experience a heightened clarity of expression in their inner voice and become more accepting of their lived experiences and their individuality. To help balance the throat chakra, practice conscious communication and vulnerability with yourself and others.

VOICE ACTIVATION
(USING YOUR VOICE)

Speaking our soul's truth is extremely powerful and has never been more important to act upon than now. We need change, and we need it now! How we proceed as a collective into our future is up to you. It is our goal to help contribute to empowering the Feminine Collective to share their voices, thoughts, hopes, and dreams so we may create a better future for ourselves and generations to come.

Our favorite throat chakra clearing guided meditation can be found on YouTube - ***Extremely Powerful* THROAT CHAKRA Healing - A Guided Meditation**

The feminine's voice has been suppressed for a long time, so it's ok if this takes you some time to activate and clear this chakra. We are all relearning how to speak up and powerfully deliver our messages. This chakra not only represents voice but also encompasses a larger concept of overall expression. The Feminine energy is creation itself, and she wants to express her perspective of the world through any creative medium.

How will you communicate who you are and your ideas?

JOURNAL

DAILY AFFIRMATIONS: I AM...

_____
_____
_____
_____
_____

WHAT AM I READY TO CREATE?

_____
_____
_____
_____
_____

VISUALIZE YOUR IDEAL REALITY AND DESCRIBE IT IN DETAIL:

_____
_____
_____
_____
_____
_____
_____
_____
_____
_____
_____

BREATHE IN

GRATITUDE: THANK THE UNIVERSE FOR GRANTING YOU...

_____
_____
_____
_____

WHAT ACTIONS CAN I TAKE TODAY TO CREATE MY DREAM
REALITY?

_____
_____
_____
_____

HOW DOES THIS NEW REALITY FEEL IN MY BODY?

_____
_____
_____
_____
_____
_____
_____
_____
_____
_____
_____
_____
_____

BREATHE OUT

WRITING FLOW: TAKE THE SPACE BELOW TO WRITE WHATEVER
COMES THROUGH YOUR MIND. NO JUDGMENT, JUST ALLOWANCE...

Throat Chakra Affirmations

IT IS SAFE FOR ME TO SPEAK MY TRUTH.

I COMMUNICATE WITH LOVE AND
SPEAK FROM MY HEART.

MY IDEAS ARE WORTHY OF EXPRESSION.

I SPEAK WITH CLARITY AND CONFIDENCE.

I CHOOSE AUTHENTICITY AND
VULNERABILITY OVER PERFECTION.

IT IS MY DIVINE RIGHT
TO SPEAK MY TRUTH.

I COMMUNICATE MY FEELINGS WITH EASE.

I EXPRESS MYSELF CREATIVELY.

I LOVE TO SHARE MY
EXPERIENCES AND WISDOM.

I AM A CHANNEL FOR DIVINE
LOVE TO BE EXPRESSED.

Third Eye Chakra

ELEMENT: **LIGHT**
COLOR: **INDIGO**

The third eye chakra is the sixth of the seven main chakras, located in the center of your forehead.

The third eye chakra serves as a tool for discerning the finer aspects of existence, transcending physical sensations, and delving into the realm of subtle energies. Activating your third eye enables you to embrace an intuitive awareness and understanding of your inner world.

When your third eye holds blockages, it can manifest as losing your sense of direction in life and distrusting your inner voice and intuition. When in balance, you can expect your intuition to be heightened, and you begin to see your life with more clarity, self- awareness, and emotional balance.

Opening Your Third Eye and Unlocking Your Intuition

The third eye chakra is perhaps the least understood chakra in Western cultures. It corresponds to an individual's pineal gland. The pineal gland is a pine cone shaped organ deep inside the brain that seems to function as the brain's radio receiver. Most of us who haven't devoted a lifetime to spiritual practice have calcified pineal glands or "Third Eyes". This is a terrible tragedy that has befallen our modern culture during the long period of time we've been kept in the dark and led astray from our own divinity.

As we work through the chakras to release energy trapped from traumas and negative programming, our energy will begin to "ascend" meaning rise up through each energy center to "awaken" our intuition and open our Third Eye. You will begin to see below the surface and have a strong sense for what is real and what is an illusion. You will be able to quickly read another's intentions and authenticity. As you strengthen this superpower, you will start to trust yourself, your perspective, and your decisions more and more. This will alter your life. All the energy spent in self-doubt, overthinking, and anxious emotions will be freed and alchemized for creating your desired reality.

But perhaps the most magical gift of all held in this energy center is the ability to access divine levels of consciousness and experience the mystical first hand. Now, let it be known that the brain is a very sophisticated system that is wired to keep you safe against all odds. If you are not firmly rooted in this reality (grounded by a happy and healthy root and sacral center), the Third Eye will most likely remain closed. But the more you practice, the more you will see. It's just like working a muscle.

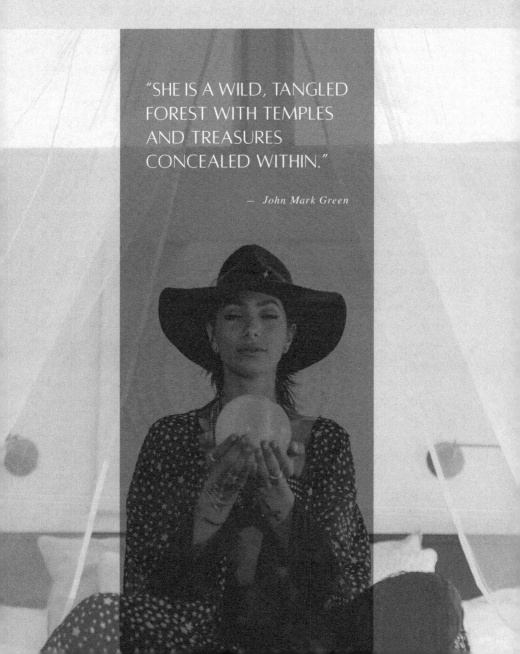

"SHE IS A WILD, TANGLED FOREST WITH TEMPLES AND TREASURES CONCEALED WITHIN."

— *John Mark Green*

In ancient cultures, the blue lotus flower was connected to Third Eye activation. It was used in rituals as a gateway to the divine. If you can get your hands on some, you can burn it, drink it in a tea, rub its oil on your face and body, or soak with it in a bath. We recommend using it in oil form and dabbing some on your Third Eye (the center of your forehead).

- Scan the QR Code above or find a 852 hz frequency via Spotify or Youtube.
- Let's begin by getting into a meditative position. Sit in a comfortable place in a private area or room, or outside in nature if you wish.
- Inhales, exhale.
- Calm and clear your mind.
- Now imagine a ball of energy at the base of your spine. You are going to move that energy with your breath to your pineal gland. Imagine it as a tiny pinecone nestled deep in the lower center of your brain.
- Exhale all the air out of your lungs completely.
- Inhale deeply into your belly, as deep as you can go, filling your chest up last.
- As you inhale, imagine yourself moving the energy from the base of your spine, up your back, to the lower center of your brain.
- With your breath, imagine you are blowing up a balloon in your brain, filling it with this energy.
- As your balloon fills all the way up, hold it.
- Exhale and release.
- As you practice this breathing technique, move your awareness to the middle of your forehead. Start to notice any movement "behind your eyes".
- What do you see? Are there swirls of energy? If yes, notice their color and patterns of movement.

The deeper you go into this practice, the more that will be revealed to you. Keep a record of what you see and watch the magic unfold. **Your Third Eye is opening.**

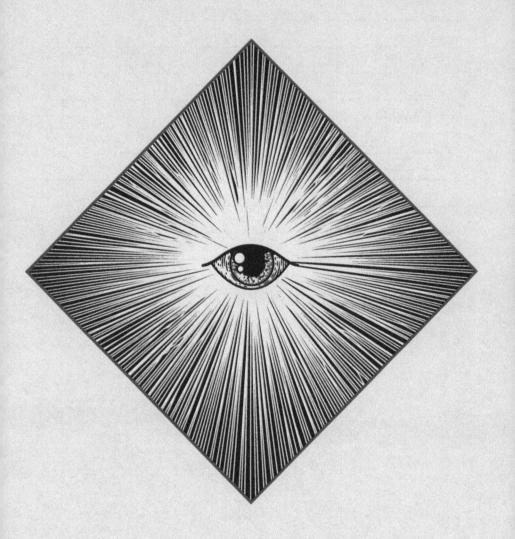

JOURNAL

DAILY AFFIRMATIONS: I AM...

_____

_____

_____

_____

_____

WHAT AM I READY TO CREATE?

_____

_____

_____

_____

_____

VISUALIZE YOUR IDEAL REALITY AND DESCRIBE IT IN DETAIL:

_____

_____

_____

_____

_____

_____

_____

_____

_____

_____

_____

BREATHE IN

GRATITUDE: THANK THE UNIVERSE FOR GRANTING YOU...

_____

_____

_____

_____

WHAT ACTIONS CAN I TAKE TODAY TO CREATE MY DREAM
REALITY?

_____

_____

_____

_____

HOW DOES THIS NEW REALITY FEEL IN MY BODY?

_____

_____

_____

_____

_____

_____

_____

_____

_____

_____

_____

_____

_____

BREATHE OUT

WRITING FLOW: TAKE THE SPACE BELOW TO WRITE WHATEVER
COMES THROUGH YOUR MIND. NO JUDGMENT, JUST ALLOWANCE...

It's time to revisit our Lover's List. Read it over. Has it changed since you first penned it?

- Scan the QR Code above or search for a 528 hz frequency via Spotify or Youtube.
- Let's begin by getting into a meditative position.
- Calm your mind and bring awareness to your breath. Breathe in, breathe out.
- Visualize your lover – a person with all the qualities on your list.
- How do they feel to you? How do they love you? Feel it in your heart and body.
- Imagine what you will do together, the healing you will bring to each other's lives, the depth you will experience.

- Visualize it, believe it.
- Bring yourself into alignment with this energy so that you can attract it. You deserve all of this and nothing less.
- Imagine the sound transforming your being into one of pure love and pure bliss.
- Let the fears, anxiety, and pain of the past melt away.

Now the tests that may arise are for you not to settle for anything less than this frequency. There may be offers or illusions put into your path meant to test your commitment to your true heart's desire. Show yourself loyalty and choose yourself always. Allow only what will bring your heart its ultimate happiness You are becoming a Queen; your equal is on the way.

Whenever you miss him or her (because they already exist out there somewhere), return to this practice and feel this person.

JOURNAL

DATE / /

DAILY AFFIRMATIONS: I AM...

_____

_____

_____

_____

_____

WHAT AM I READY TO CREATE?

_____

_____

_____

_____

_____

VISUALIZE YOUR IDEAL REALITY AND DESCRIBE IT IN DETAIL:

_____

_____

_____

_____

_____

_____

_____

_____

_____

_____

_____

BREATHE IN

GRATITUDE: THANK THE UNIVERSE FOR GRANTING YOU...

_____
_____
_____
_____

WHAT ACTIONS CAN I TAKE TODAY TO CREATE MY DREAM
REALITY?

_____
_____
_____
_____

HOW DOES THIS NEW REALITY FEEL IN MY BODY?

_____
_____
_____
_____
_____
_____
_____
_____
_____
_____
_____
_____
_____
_____

BREATHE OUT

WRITING FLOW: TAKE THE SPACE BELOW TO WRITE WHATEVER
COMES THROUGH YOUR MIND. NO JUDGMENT, JUST ALLOWANCE...

Third Eye Affirmations

I TRUST MY INTUITION TO REVEAL THE PATH
I'M MEANT TO WALK IN LIFE.

I AM CONNECTED TO MY PURPOSE AND MY TRUE PATH.

I SEE BEYOND WHAT IS APPARENT
TO WHAT IS REALLY THERE.

I CARRY THE SEEDS OF WISDOM TO SEE ALL THAT IS,
ALL THAT WAS, AND ALL THAT WILL BE.

I EMBRACE THE SUBCONSCIOUS
TRUTH THAT MY DREAMS REVEAL.

I BELIEVE IN THE POWER OF MY IMAGINATION TO SHOW
ME THAT ANYTHING IS POSSIBLE.

WITH LOVE AS MY INNER GUIDE,
I WELCOME HEALING AND STEP INTO LIGHT.

I AM DIVINE

JOURNAL

DAILY AFFIRMATIONS: I AM...

_____

_____

_____

_____

_____

WHAT AM I READY TO CREATE?

_____

_____

_____

_____

_____

VISUALIZE YOUR IDEAL REALITY AND DESCRIBE IT IN DETAIL:

_____

_____

_____

_____

_____

_____

_____

_____

_____

_____

_____

BREATHE IN

GRATITUDE: THANK THE UNIVERSE FOR GRANTING YOU...

_____
_____
_____

_____

WHAT ACTIONS CAN I TAKE TODAY TO CREATE MY DREAM
REALITY?

_____
_____
_____

_____

HOW DOES THIS NEW REALITY FEEL IN MY BODY?

_____
_____
_____
_____
_____
_____
_____
_____
_____
_____
_____
_____
_____
_____

BREATHE OUT

156

WRITING FLOW: TAKE THE SPACE BELOW TO WRITE WHATEVER COMES THROUGH YOUR MIND. NO JUDGMENT, JUST ALLOWANCE...

"YOU WERE NOT ORIGINALLY DESIGNED TO SUFFER OR BE IN WANT OF ANYTHING. SOPHIA – THE ONE DIVINE MOTHER CREATRIX OF ALL LIFE – DESIGNED YOU TO LIVE IN HARMONY AS A SOVEREIGN CO-CREATOR WITH THE OVERFLOWING ABUNDANCE OF THIS PLANET. YOUR DIVINE INHERITANCE INCLUDES ALL OF YOUR EARTHLY NEEDS BEING MET, AS WELL AS RECEIVING ALL OF YOUR HEART'S DESIRES. IT IS HER DIVINE WILL FOR YOU TO PROSPER IN EVERY AREA OF YOUR LIFE."

– *Transmission from the Goddess Isis taken from "The Sophia Code"*

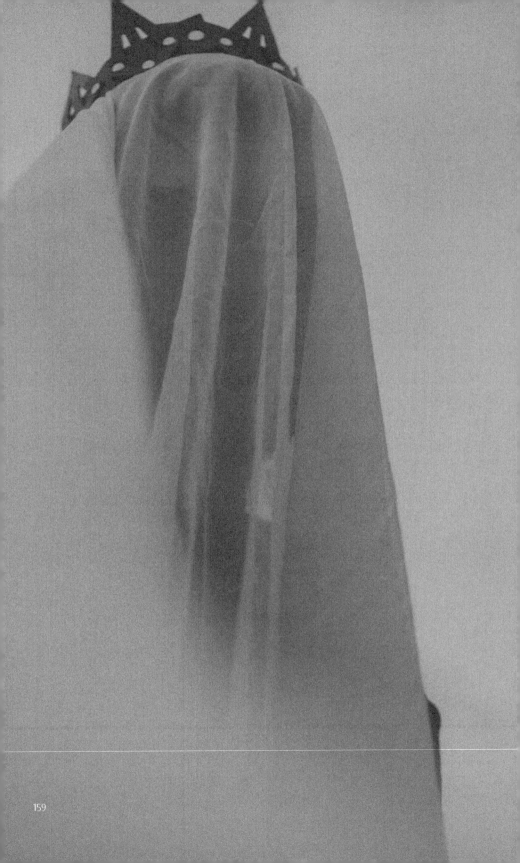

CROWN CHAKRA

ELEMENT: **THOUGHT**
COLOR: **WHITE**

The crown chakra is located at the top of the head and is the final energy center of the seven, associated with enlightenment, spirituality and psychic abilities. This energy center corresponds to your connection with "Spirit," "Source," God," "Creator," as well as your sense of universal consciousness, wisdom, self-awareness, and unity.

When the crown chakra is in balance, you will feel a profound and deep connection with the seen and unseen all around you. This sense of connection with the Universe, yourself, and all that it is cultivates and fosters a clear understanding of your purpose in this life.

An imbalanced crown chakra can manifest as signs like heightened ego, a lack of empathy, or feelings of disconnection from your higher power. An individual who has learned to ground themselves and worked through a significant amount of their shadow may begin to energetically expand their crown chakra, as energy is freed from blockages.

As the crown chakra expands it becomes eligible to receive higher levels of information that are then passed down to the Third Eye to be, for lack of a better term, decoded. This phenomena is known as the highly prized **mystical experience**. Once considered to be an extremely rare occurrence, experiencing the Divine directly is becoming more and more common as the planet spiritually awakens.

While a mystical experience may challenge your belief system, it will free you from the narrative that your access to God/Source/Universe is dependent on someone else, removing the middleman from your path. A spiritual guide or mentor is always recommended to help you interpret and integrate these experiences, however we strongly warn against anyone whose intentions are to manipulate, control or keep you codependent in the name of God no matter their title be it guru, teacher, priest, or shaman.

JOURNAL

DATE / /

DAILY AFFIRMATIONS: I AM...

_____
_____
_____
_____
_____

WHAT AM I READY TO CREATE?

_____
_____
_____
_____
_____

VISUALIZE YOUR IDEAL REALITY AND DESCRIBE IT IN DETAIL:

_____
_____
_____
_____
_____
_____
_____
_____
_____
_____
_____

BREATHE IN

GRATITUDE: THANK THE UNIVERSE FOR GRANTING YOU...

_____

_____

_____

_____

WHAT ACTIONS CAN I TAKE TODAY TO CREATE MY DREAM
REALITY?

_____

_____

_____

_____

HOW DOES THIS NEW REALITY FEEL IN MY BODY?

_____

_____

_____

_____

_____

_____

_____

_____

_____

_____

_____

_____

_____

_____

BREATHE OUT

WRITING FLOW: TAKE THE SPACE BELOW TO WRITE WHATEVER
COMES THROUGH YOUR MIND. NO JUDGMENT, JUST ALLOWANCE...

"THROUGH THE POWER OF MY OWN FORGIVENESS, I NOW SET MYSELF FREE FROM FOLLOWING UNCONSCIOUS BELIEFS ABOUT RELIGION, SPIRITUALITY, AND GOD:

I FORGIVE MYSELF FOR BELIEVING THAT MY HUMANITY IS A FALLEN STATE OF SIN.

I FORGIVE MYSELF FOR STRUGGLING AGAINST MYSELF FOR A DIVINE POWER THAT ALREADY EXISTS WITHIN ME.

I FORGIVE MYSELF FOR STRIVING TO SAVE A GOD OF OMNISCIENT POWER THAT IS THE ETERNAL SOURCE OF UNCONDITIONAL DIVINE LOVE.

I FORGIVE MYSELF FOR THE DESTITUTION CREATED BY VOWS OF POVERTY THAT HAVE KEPT ME SEPARATED FROM THE ABUNDANT, PROSPEROUS GODSELF WITHIN ME.

I FORGIVE MYSELF FOR SEEKING APPROVAL OUTSIDE OF THE WORTHINESS OF MY TRUE DIVINE SELF.

I FORGIVE MYSELF FOR FORGETTING THAT HEAVEN IS ALWAYS WITHIN ME."

     — *Transmission from the Goddess Isis taken from "The Sophia Code"*

You're made out of stardust ...

... can you see now,
HOW BEAUTIFUL YOU ARE?

TRUSTING THE UNIVERSE
AND RETURNING TO ONENESS

"THE WAY TO BECOME ONE WITH THE UNIVERSE IS TO TRUST IT."

– *Alan Watts*

As you embark on this path of remembrance, one of the most powerful tools you can learn and cultivate is trust. The Universe is conspiring for you, not against you. When things don't appear to be working out in your favor, return to this place of knowing. Trust that the Universe is capable of miracles and is working behind the scenes to bring you your desires. Trust that its power is greater than we can ever imagine, and its love for you is infinite.

You are becoming the co-creator of your own destiny. You may not be able to predict "how" or "when" the cosmos will get your orders to you, but know that it will. As your mind, body, and spirit begin to synchronize and move into alignment with your highest path, you will begin to see repeating numbers such as 1111, 2222, 3333, 4444, 5555, 7777, 8888, and 9999. While the meaning of each is unique to the individual experiencing them, take it as a sign of confirmation from the Universe that the work you are doing is working and that your angels/spirit guides/ancestors are guiding you. When you see these signs from the Universe, stop for a moment to acknowledge and express gratitude in whatever way feels best. With gratitude comes abundance.

Guided Meditation #8
Becoming One with the Universe

- Scan the QR Code above or find a 963 hz frequency via Spotify or Youtube.
- Let's start by sitting in a comfortable position in a private area or room, or outside in nature if you wish.
- Begin with deep inhales and exhales.
- Calm and clear your mind.
- Exhale any tension your body is holding on to.
- Imagine a violet stream of light entering your body through the top of your head.
- Imagine it filling your entire being with violet light.
- Feel your body become this violet light.

- As you become this violet energy ball, imagine yourself expanding.
- Expand enough to hold the room you are sitting in within you.
- Expand further until you encompass the house you are living in, the city your house is in. The county, the state, the continent, until eventually the world is within you.
- Begin to merge your being with the Universe itself. Become one with it. Look around at your creation.
- Everything you need is within you.

As the third eye and crown chakras begin to work together synergistically, your natural born psychic gifts may also come online. But this is the beginning of another journey for a different day...

We are proud and honored to have walked with you this far. Remember to trust that no matter how things may seem, your desires are on their way. The Universe works in mysterious ways, have patience and let the mystery unfold.

JOURNAL

DAILY AFFIRMATIONS: I AM...

_____
_____
_____
_____
_____

WHAT AM I READY TO CREATE?

_____
_____
_____
_____
_____

VISUALIZE YOUR IDEAL REALITY AND DESCRIBE IT IN DETAIL:

_____
_____
_____
_____
_____
_____
_____
_____
_____
_____
_____

BREATHE IN

GRATITUDE: THANK THE UNIVERSE FOR GRANTING YOU...

_____
_____
_____
_____

WHAT ACTIONS CAN I TAKE TODAY TO CREATE MY DREAM REALITY?

_____
_____
_____
_____

HOW DOES THIS NEW REALITY FEEL IN MY BODY?

_____
_____
_____
_____
_____
_____
_____
_____
_____
_____
_____
_____
_____

BREATHE OUT

WRITING FLOW: TAKE THE SPACE BELOW TO WRITE WHATEVER
COMES THROUGH YOUR MIND. NO JUDGMENT, JUST ALLOWANCE...

"I FORGIVE MYSELF FOR FEARING THAT I WILL DIE FOR EMBODYING MY PERSONAL POWER.

I FORGIVE MYSELF FOR SUFFOCATING MY OWN VOICE TO PREVENT THE FULL EXPRESSION OF MY PERSONAL POWER.

I FORGIVE MYSELF FOR DREADING AN OUTCOME OF ISOLATION FOR LIVING IN MY PERSONAL POWER.

I FORGIVE MYSELF FOR THE ACTS OF SELF–REJECTION AND SHAMING OF MY HUMAN BODY THAT I COMMITTED TO BLATANTLY RESIST EMBODYING MY PERSONAL POWER.

I FORGIVE MYSELF FOR RELINQUISHING MY PERSONAL POWER TO BLESS OTHERS AND MYSELF."

— *Transmission from the Goddess Isis taken from "The Sophia Code"*

You made it to the end, our beautiful friend.

Actually, you made it to a new beginning.

A NEW OPENING AND OPPORTUNITY.

To lean in to yourself, your challenges, to your heart, to your dreams, and your desires.

When you reach the "end" of something, you are merely at the entrance of a new beginning.

A NEW LIFE.

A NEW WAY OF BEING.

And you have the choice to take what you learned in this journal,

Or to close it, forget it, and never open it again.

But remember, As a sovereign, limitless being.

You have the power within to shift worlds.

And all it takes is a **SEED TO BE PLANTED AND AN EMBER TO BE SPARKED** within the depths of your heart and soul.

So allow these new seeds of awareness and change to be planted.

And remember that **NATURE TAKES HER TIME.**

Any seed planted needs nurturing, patience, love, and time to grow into an admirable, miraculous flower.

Her roots grow thicker, moving deeper into the ground, while simultaneously unraveling up and reaching for the light.

And you are a part of nature.

So water your inner garden.

Honor your seasons.

Embrace your challenges.

Love your shadows.

And be patient with yourself as you transform from seeds to a flower that **embraces her magnificence and divine expression of creation.**

JOURNAL

DATE / /

DAILY AFFIRMATIONS: I AM...

_____
_____
_____
_____
_____

WHAT AM I READY TO CREATE?

_____
_____
_____
_____
_____

VISUALIZE YOUR IDEAL REALITY AND DESCRIBE IT IN DETAIL:

_____
_____
_____
_____
_____
_____
_____
_____
_____
_____
_____

BREATHE IN

GRATITUDE: THANK THE UNIVERSE FOR GRANTING YOU...

_____
_____
_____
_____

WHAT ACTIONS CAN I TAKE TODAY TO CREATE MY DREAM
REALITY?

_____
_____
_____
_____

HOW DOES THIS NEW REALITY FEEL IN MY BODY?

_____
_____
_____
_____
_____
_____
_____
_____
_____
_____
_____
_____
_____

BREATHE OUT

WRITING FLOW: TAKE THE SPACE BELOW TO WRITE WHATEVER
COMES THROUGH YOUR MIND. NO JUDGMENT, JUST ALLOWANCE...

"I ACCEPT THAT I HOLD THE GOLDEN KEYS TO MY HEAVEN
OF EARTH.

I ACCEPT THAT I CREATE MY REALITY, BY THE POWER OF
MY WORD.

MY WORD IS GOOD, MY HEART IS PURE.

BY THE LOVING POWER OF MY PURE WORD I CALL FORTH
AND INVOKE THE FULL PRESENCE OF FORGIVENESS WITHIN
MYSELF."

— *Transmission from the Goddess Isis taken from "The Sophia Code"*

JOURNAL

DATE / /

DAILY AFFIRMATIONS: I AM...

_____
_____
_____
_____
_____

WHAT AM I READY TO CREATE?

_____
_____
_____
_____
_____

VISUALIZE YOUR IDEAL REALITY AND DESCRIBE IT IN DETAIL:

_____
_____
_____
_____
_____
_____
_____
_____
_____
_____

BREATHE IN

GRATITUDE: THANK THE UNIVERSE FOR GRANTING YOU...

_____

_____

_____

_____

WHAT ACTIONS CAN I TAKE TODAY TO CREATE MY DREAM
REALITY?

_____

_____

_____

_____

HOW DOES THIS NEW REALITY FEEL IN MY BODY?

_____

_____

_____

_____

_____

_____

_____

_____

_____

_____

_____

_____

_____

BREATHE OUT

WRITING FLOW: TAKE THE SPACE BELOW TO WRITE WHATEVER
COMES THROUGH YOUR MIND. NO JUDGMENT, JUST ALLOWANCE...

JOURNAL

DATE / /

DAILY AFFIRMATIONS: I AM...

_____
_____
_____
_____
_____

WHAT AM I READY TO CREATE?

_____
_____
_____
_____
_____

VISUALIZE YOUR IDEAL REALITY AND DESCRIBE IT IN DETAIL:

_____
_____
_____
_____
_____
_____
_____
_____
_____
_____

BREATHE IN

GRATITUDE: THANK THE UNIVERSE FOR GRANTING YOU...

_____

_____

_____

_____

WHAT ACTIONS CAN I TAKE TODAY TO CREATE MY DREAM
REALITY?

_____

_____

_____

_____

HOW DOES THIS NEW REALITY FEEL IN MY BODY?

_____

_____

_____

_____

_____

_____

_____

_____

_____

_____

_____

_____

_____

_____

BREATHE OUT

WRITING FLOW: TAKE THE SPACE BELOW TO WRITE WHATEVER
COMES THROUGH YOUR MIND. NO JUDGMENT, JUST ALLOWANCE...

_____

_____

_____

_____

_____

_____

_____

_____

_____

_____

_____

_____

_____

_____

_____

_____

_____

_____

_____

_____

_____

_____

_____

_____

JOURNAL

DATE / /

DAILY AFFIRMATIONS: I AM...

_____

_____

_____

_____

_____

WHAT AM I READY TO CREATE?

_____

_____

_____

_____

_____

VISUALIZE YOUR IDEAL REALITY AND DESCRIBE IT IN DETAIL:

_____

_____

_____

_____

_____

_____

_____

_____

_____

_____

_____

187

BREATHE IN

GRATITUDE: THANK THE UNIVERSE FOR GRANTING YOU...

_____
_____
_____
_____

WHAT ACTIONS CAN I TAKE TODAY TO CREATE MY DREAM
REALITY?

_____
_____
_____
_____

HOW DOES THIS NEW REALITY FEEL IN MY BODY?

_____
_____
_____
_____
_____
_____
_____
_____
_____
_____
_____
_____
_____
_____

BREATHE OUT

WRITING FLOW: TAKE THE SPACE BELOW TO WRITE WHATEVER
COMES THROUGH YOUR MIND. NO JUDGMENT, JUST ALLOWANCE...

JOURNAL

DATE / /

DAILY AFFIRMATIONS: I AM...

_____
_____
_____
_____
_____

WHAT AM I READY TO CREATE?

_____
_____
_____
_____
_____

VISUALIZE YOUR IDEAL REALITY AND DESCRIBE IT IN DETAIL:

_____
_____
_____
_____
_____
_____
_____
_____
_____
_____

BREATHE IN

GRATITUDE: THANK THE UNIVERSE FOR GRANTING YOU...

_____

_____

_____

_____

WHAT ACTIONS CAN I TAKE TODAY TO CREATE MY DREAM
REALITY?

_____

_____

_____

_____

HOW DOES THIS NEW REALITY FEEL IN MY BODY?

_____

_____

_____

_____

_____

_____

_____

_____

_____

_____

_____

_____

_____

BREATHE OUT

WRITING FLOW: TAKE THE SPACE BELOW TO WRITE WHATEVER
COMES THROUGH YOUR MIND. NO JUDGMENT, JUST ALLOWANCE...

JOURNAL

DAILY AFFIRMATIONS: I AM...

_____
_____
_____
_____
_____

WHAT AM I READY TO CREATE?

_____
_____
_____
_____
_____

VISUALIZE YOUR IDEAL REALITY AND DESCRIBE IT IN DETAIL:

_____
_____
_____
_____
_____
_____
_____
_____
_____
_____
_____
_____

BREATHE IN

GRATITUDE: THANK THE UNIVERSE FOR GRANTING YOU...

_____

_____

_____

_____

WHAT ACTIONS CAN I TAKE TODAY TO CREATE MY DREAM
REALITY?

_____

_____

_____

_____

HOW DOES THIS NEW REALITY FEEL IN MY BODY?

_____

_____

_____

_____

_____

_____

_____

_____

_____

_____

_____

_____

_____

_____

BREATHE OUT

WRITING FLOW: TAKE THE SPACE BELOW TO WRITE WHATEVER
COMES THROUGH YOUR MIND. NO JUDGMENT, JUST ALLOWANCE...

JOURNAL

DATE / /

DAILY AFFIRMATIONS: I AM...

_____
_____
_____
_____
_____

WHAT AM I READY TO CREATE?

_____
_____
_____
_____
_____

VISUALIZE YOUR IDEAL REALITY AND DESCRIBE IT IN DETAIL:

_____
_____
_____
_____
_____
_____
_____
_____
_____
_____
_____

BREATHE IN

GRATITUDE: THANK THE UNIVERSE FOR GRANTING YOU...

_____
_____
_____
_____

WHAT ACTIONS CAN I TAKE TODAY TO CREATE MY DREAM
REALITY?

_____
_____
_____
_____

HOW DOES THIS NEW REALITY FEEL IN MY BODY?

_____
_____
_____
_____
_____
_____
_____
_____
_____
_____
_____
_____
_____

BREATHE OUT

WRITING FLOW: TAKE THE SPACE BELOW TO WRITE WHATEVER
COMES THROUGH YOUR MIND. NO JUDGMENT, JUST ALLOWANCE...

JOURNAL

DAILY AFFIRMATIONS: I AM...

_____

_____

_____

_____

_____

WHAT AM I READY TO CREATE?

_____

_____

_____

_____

_____

VISUALIZE YOUR IDEAL REALITY AND DESCRIBE IT IN DETAIL:

_____

_____

_____

_____

_____

_____

_____

_____

_____

_____

_____

BREATHE IN

GRATITUDE: THANK THE UNIVERSE FOR GRANTING YOU...

_____

_____

_____

_____

WHAT ACTIONS CAN I TAKE TODAY TO CREATE MY DREAM
REALITY?

_____

_____

_____

_____

HOW DOES THIS NEW REALITY FEEL IN MY BODY?

_____

_____

_____

_____

_____

_____

_____

_____

_____

_____

_____

_____

_____

_____

BREATHE OUT

WRITING FLOW: TAKE THE SPACE BELOW TO WRITE WHATEVER
COMES THROUGH YOUR MIND. NO JUDGMENT, JUST ALLOWANCE...

JOURNAL

DATE / /

DAILY AFFIRMATIONS: I AM...

_____

_____

_____

_____

_____

WHAT AM I READY TO CREATE?

_____

_____

_____

_____

_____

VISUALIZE YOUR IDEAL REALITY AND DESCRIBE IT IN DETAIL:

_____

_____

_____

_____

_____

_____

_____

_____

_____

_____

BREATHE IN

GRATITUDE: THANK THE UNIVERSE FOR GRANTING YOU...

_____
_____
_____
_____

WHAT ACTIONS CAN I TAKE TODAY TO CREATE MY DREAM
REALITY?

_____
_____
_____
_____

HOW DOES THIS NEW REALITY FEEL IN MY BODY?

_____
_____
_____
_____
_____
_____
_____
_____
_____
_____
_____
_____
_____
_____

BREATHE OUT

WRITING FLOW: TAKE THE SPACE BELOW TO WRITE WHATEVER
COMES THROUGH YOUR MIND. NO JUDGMENT, JUST ALLOWANCE...

JOURNAL

DATE / /

DAILY AFFIRMATIONS: I AM...

_____

_____

_____

_____

_____

WHAT AM I READY TO CREATE?

_____

_____

_____

_____

_____

VISUALIZE YOUR IDEAL REALITY AND DESCRIBE IT IN DETAIL:

_____

_____

_____

_____

_____

_____

_____

_____

_____

_____

_____

_____

BREATHE IN

GRATITUDE: THANK THE UNIVERSE FOR GRANTING YOU...

_____

_____

_____

_____

WHAT ACTIONS CAN I TAKE TODAY TO CREATE MY DREAM
REALITY?

_____

_____

_____

_____

HOW DOES THIS NEW REALITY FEEL IN MY BODY?

_____

_____

_____

_____

_____

_____

_____

_____

_____

_____

_____

_____

BREATHE OUT

JOURNAL

DAILY AFFIRMATIONS: I AM...

_____

_____

_____

_____

_____

WHAT AM I READY TO CREATE?

_____

_____

_____

_____

_____

VISUALIZE YOUR IDEAL REALITY AND DESCRIBE IT IN DETAIL:

_____

_____

_____

_____

_____

_____

_____

_____

_____

_____

_____

BREATHE IN

GRATITUDE: THANK THE UNIVERSE FOR GRANTING YOU...

_____
_____
_____
_____

WHAT ACTIONS CAN I TAKE TODAY TO CREATE MY DREAM
REALITY?

_____
_____
_____
_____

HOW DOES THIS NEW REALITY FEEL IN MY BODY?

_____
_____
_____
_____
_____
_____
_____
_____
_____
_____
_____
_____
_____

BREATHE OUT

JOURNAL

DATE / /

DAILY AFFIRMATIONS: I AM...

_____
_____
_____
_____
_____

WHAT AM I READY TO CREATE?

_____
_____
_____
_____
_____

VISUALIZE YOUR IDEAL REALITY AND DESCRIBE IT IN DETAIL:

_____
_____
_____
_____
_____
_____
_____
_____
_____
_____
_____
_____

BREATHE IN

GRATITUDE: THANK THE UNIVERSE FOR GRANTING YOU...

_____
_____
_____
_____

WHAT ACTIONS CAN I TAKE TODAY TO CREATE MY DREAM
REALITY?

_____
_____
_____
_____

HOW DOES THIS NEW REALITY FEEL IN MY BODY?

_____
_____
_____
_____
_____
_____
_____
_____
_____
_____
_____
_____
_____

BREATHE OUT

WRITING FLOW: TAKE THE SPACE BELOW TO WRITE WHATEVER
COMES THROUGH YOUR MIND. NO JUDGMENT, JUST ALLOWANCE...

Made in United States
Orlando, FL
17 December 2024

56066253R00134